LEVEL FIFTEEN

FRACTIONS

SO-CAJ-339

Developmental Mathematics

Solution Manual

L. George Saad, Ph. D.
Professor Emeritus
Long Island University

1 CHANGING INTO A SMALLER FRACTIONAL UNIT

Example 1.

The figure to the right is divided into fourths.
One fourth is shaded.

- If each one fourth is divided into 2 equal parts, the figure becomes 8 eighths.

  1 fourth becomes 2 eighths.

- If each one fourth is divided into 3 equal parts, the figure becomes 12 twelfths.

  1 fourth becomes 3 twelfths.

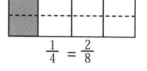
$$\frac{1}{4} = \frac{2}{8}$$
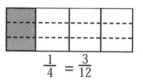
$$\frac{1}{4} = \frac{3}{12}$$

Example 2.

The figure is divided into halves.
One half is shaded.
Divide each one half into 2 equal parts.

| The whole becomes | 4 fourths. |
| One-half becomes | 2 fourths. |

$$\frac{1}{2} = \frac{2}{4}$$

Example 3.

The figure is divided into thirds.
One third is shaded.
Divide each one third into 4 equal parts.

| The whole becomes | 12 twelfths. |
| One third becomes | 4 twelfths. |

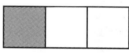
$$\frac{1}{3} = \frac{4}{12}$$
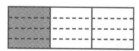

Example 4.

The figure is divided into sevenths.
One seventh is shaded.
Divide each one seventh into 5 equal parts.

| The whole becomes | 35 thirty fifths. |
| One seventh becomes | 5 thirty fifths. |

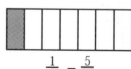
$$\frac{1}{7} = \frac{5}{35}$$
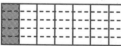

© Copyright by L. George Saad

APPLICATIONS

1. The figure is divided into fourths.
1 fourth is shaded.

Make the whole into 12 twelfths.

1 fourth is made into __3 twelfths.__

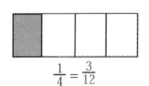

$$\frac{1}{4} = \frac{3}{12}$$

2. The figure is divided into fifths.
1 fifth is shaded.

Make the whole into twentieths.

1 fifth is made into __4 twentieths.__

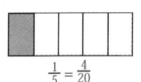

$$\frac{1}{5} = \frac{4}{20}$$

3. The figure is divided into thirds.
1 third is shaded.

Make the whole into eighteenths.

1 third is made into __6 eighteenths.__

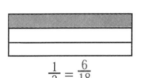

$$\frac{1}{3} = \frac{6}{18}$$

4.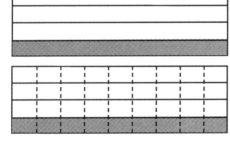

4 fourths become __36 thirty sixths.__
1 fourth becomes __9 thirty sixths.__

5.

6 sixths become __24 twenty fourths.__
1 sixth becomes __4 twenty fourths.__

6. Write the missing number.

a. $\frac{1}{3} = \frac{4}{12}$ b. $\frac{1}{5} = \frac{3}{15}$ c. $\frac{1}{8} = \frac{7}{56}$ d. $\frac{1}{9} = \frac{2}{18}$

e. $\frac{1}{3} = \frac{5}{15}$ f. $\frac{1}{6} = \frac{5}{30}$ g. $\frac{1}{10} = \frac{4}{40}$ h. $\frac{1}{7} = \frac{6}{42}$

i. $\frac{1}{9} = \frac{5}{45}$ j. $\frac{1}{8} = \frac{10}{80}$ k. $\frac{1}{5} = \frac{17}{85}$ l. $\frac{1}{12} = \frac{9}{108}$

© Copyright by L. George Saad   **Level 15**

Example 5.

The figure is divided into fifths.
2 fifths are shaded.

Divide each one-fifth into 4 equal parts,
The whole becomes 20 twentieths.
2 fifths become 8 twentieths.

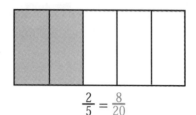

$$\frac{2}{5} = \frac{8}{20}$$

Example 6.

The figure is divided into fourths.
3 fourths are shaded.
Divide each one fourth into 5 equal parts,
The whole becomes 20 twentieths.
3 fourths become 15 twentieths.

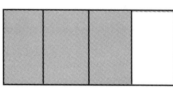

$$\frac{3}{4} = \frac{15}{20}$$

Example 7.

The figure is divided into thirds.
2 thirds are shaded.
Divide each one-third into 4 equal parts.
The whole becomes 12 twelfths.
2 thirds become ___8___ twelfths.

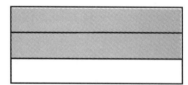

$$\frac{2}{3} = \frac{8}{12}$$

Example 8.

The figure is divided into sixths.
5 sixths are colored.
- If you divide each one-sixth into 2 equal parts,
  the whole becomes 12 twelfths.
  5 sixths become 10 twelfths.
- If you divide each one-sixth into 3 equal parts,
  the whole becomes 18 eighteenths.
  5 sixths become **15 eighteenths.**
- If you divide each one-sixth into 5 equal parts,
  the whole becomes 30 thirtieths.
  5 sixths become **25 thirtieths**

© Copyright by L. George Saad

APPLICATIONS

1. The figure is divided into ninths.
   4 ninths are shaded.

   You make the ninths into eighteenths.
   1 ninth is made into **2 eighteenths.** $\frac{1}{9} = \frac{2}{18}$
   4 ninths are made into **8 eighteenths.** $\frac{4}{9} = \frac{8}{18}$

2. The figure is divided into sevenths.
   3 sevenths are shaded.

   You make the sevenths into fourteenths.
   1 seventh is made into **2 fourteenths.** $\frac{1}{7} = \frac{2}{14}$
   3 sevenths are made into **6 fourteenths.** $\frac{3}{7} = \frac{6}{14}$

3. The figure is divided into thirds.
   2 thirds are shaded.

   - If you make the figure into sixths, what
     fraction of the figure would be shaded?   **4-sixths**

   - If you make the figure into ninths, what
     fractions of the figure would be shaded?   **6-ninths**

   - If you make the figure into twelfths, what
     fractions of the figure would be shaded?   **8-twelfths**

   - If you make the figure into fifteenths, what
     fraction of the figure would be shaded?   **10-fifteenths**

4. Write the missing number:
   a. $\frac{5}{8} = \frac{15}{24}$

   b. $\frac{6}{7} = \frac{30}{35}$

   c. $\frac{3}{10} = \frac{9}{30}$

   d. $\frac{2}{7} = \frac{6}{21}$

   e. $\frac{5}{11} = \frac{25}{55}$

   f. $\frac{9}{20} = \frac{45}{100}$

   g. $\frac{4}{5} = \frac{8}{10} = \frac{40}{50}$

   h. $\frac{8}{12} = \frac{40}{60} = \frac{16}{24}$

   i. $\frac{3}{8} = \frac{24}{64} = \frac{15}{40}$

   j. $\frac{5}{6} = \frac{20}{24} = \frac{25}{30}$

   k. $\frac{2}{9} = \frac{10}{45} = \frac{8}{36}$

   l. $\frac{7}{10} = \frac{70}{100} = \frac{700}{1000}$

© Copyright by L. George Saad

Level 15

2 CHANGING INTO A LARGER FRACTIONAL UNIT

Example 1.

The figure to the right is divided into 15 equal parts.
Each part is $\frac{1}{15}$ of the whole.

We may group each 3 fifteenths.
The whole becomes 5 equal parts.
Each part is $\frac{1}{5}$ of the whole.
3 fifteenths become 1 fifth.

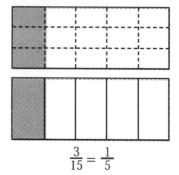

$$\frac{3}{15} = \frac{1}{5}$$

Example 2.

The figure to the right is divided into 14 equal parts.
Each part is $\frac{1}{14}$ of the whole.

We may group each 2 fourteenths.
The whole becomes 7 equal parts.
Each part is $\frac{1}{7}$ of the whole.
2 fourteenths become 1 seventh.

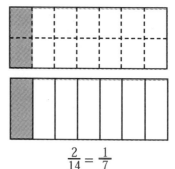

$$\frac{2}{14} = \frac{1}{7}$$

Example 3.

The figure to the right is divided into 18 equal parts.
Each part is $\frac{1}{18}$ of the whole.

• We may group each 2 eighteenths.
  The whole becomes 9 equal parts.
  Each part is $\frac{1}{9}$ of the whole.
  2 eighteenths become 1 ninth. $\quad \frac{2}{18} = \frac{1}{9}$

• We may group each 3 ninths.
  The whole becomes 3 equal parts.
  Each part is $\frac{1}{3}$ of the whole.
  3 ninths become 1 third. $\quad \frac{3}{9} = \frac{1}{3}$

• We may start by grouping each 6 eighteenths.
  The whole becomes 3 equal parts.
  Each part is $\frac{1}{3}$ of the whole.
  6 eighteenths become 1 third. $\quad \frac{6}{18} = \frac{1}{3}$

© Copyright by L. George Saad

APPLICATIONS

1. The figure is divided into sixths.
   Group each 2 sixths.
   The whole becomes __3 equal parts__
   Each part is __1-third__ of the whole.

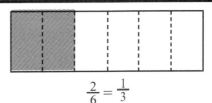

$$\frac{2}{6} = \frac{1}{3}$$

2. The figure is divided into eighths.
   Group each 4 eighths.
   The whole becomes __2 equal parts__
   Each part is __1-half__ of the whole.

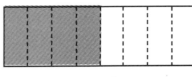

$$\frac{4}{8} = \frac{1}{2}$$

3. The figure is divided into twenty-fourths.
   a. Group each 2 twenty-fourths.
      The whole becomes __12 equal parts__
      Each part is __1-twelfth__ of the whole.

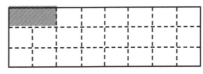

$$\frac{2}{24} = \frac{1}{12}$$

   b. Group each 3 twenty-fourths.
      The whole becomes __8 equal parts__
      Each part is __1-eighth__ of the whole.

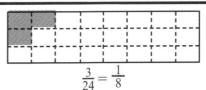

$$\frac{3}{24} = \frac{1}{8}$$

   c. Group each 4 twenty-fourths
      The whole becomes __6 equal parts__
      Each part is __1-sixth__ of the whole.

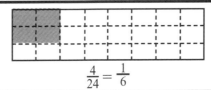

$$\frac{4}{24} = \frac{1}{6}$$

   d. Group each 6 twenty-fourths.
      The whole becomes __4 equal parts__
      Each part is __1-fourth__ of the whole.

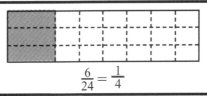

$$\frac{6}{24} = \frac{1}{4}$$

4. The figure is divided into thirtieths.
   You may group the thirtieths in different ways.

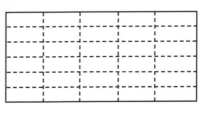

$$\frac{2}{30} = \frac{1}{15} \qquad \frac{3}{30} = \frac{1}{10} \qquad \frac{10}{30} = \frac{1}{3}$$

$$\frac{5}{30} = \frac{1}{6} \qquad \frac{6}{30} = \frac{1}{5} \qquad \frac{15}{30} = \frac{1}{2}$$

© Copyright by L. George Saad

A

Example 4.

The figure is divided into fifteenths.
6 fifteenths are shaded.

We may group each 3 fifteenths.
The whole becomes 5 fifths.
The shaded area becomes 2 fifths.

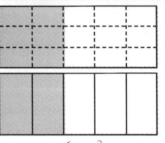

$$\frac{6}{15} = \frac{2}{5}$$

Example 5.

The figure is divided into twelfths.
8 twelfths are shaded.

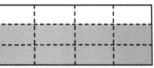

a. We may group each 2 twelfths.
   The figure becomes 6 sixths.
   The shaded area becomes 4 sixths.

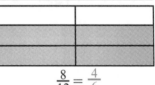

$$\frac{8}{12} = \frac{4}{6}$$

b. We may group each 4 twelfths.
   The figure becomes 3 thirds.
   The shaded area becomes 2 thirds.

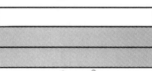

$$\frac{8}{12} = \frac{2}{3}$$

c. We may group each 3 twelfths.
   The figure becomes 4 fourths.
   We are unable to decide how many
   fourths are shaded.

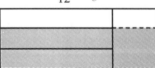

Example 6.

The figure is divided into twenty-fourths.
18 twenty-fourths are shaded.

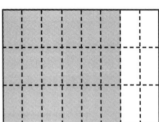

• If you group each 2 twenty-fourths,
  the figure becomes 12 twelfths.
  The shaded area becomes 9 twelfths. $\frac{18}{24} = \frac{9}{12}$

• If you group each 3 twenty-fourths,
  the figure becomes 8 eighths.
  The shaded area becomes 6 eighths. $\frac{18}{24} = \frac{6}{8}$

• If you group each 6 twenty-fourths, the figure becomes 4 fourths.
  The shaded area becomes 3 fourths. $\frac{18}{24} = \frac{3}{4}$

© Copyright by L. George Saad

APPLICATIONS

1. The figure is divided into tenths.
   4 tenths are shaded.
   Group each 2 tenths.
   The whole becomes **5 fifths.**
   The shaded area becomes **2 fifths.**

   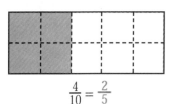
   $\frac{4}{10} = \frac{2}{5}$

2. The figure is divided into twenty-fourths.
   18 twenty-fourths are shaded.

   Group each 3 twenty-fourths.
   The shaded area becomes **6 eighths.**

   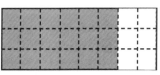
   $\frac{18}{24} = \frac{6}{8}$

3. The figure is divided into eighteenths.
   12 eighteenths are shaded.

   Group each 2 eighteenths.
   The shaded area becomes **6 ninths.**

   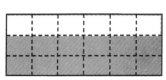
   $\frac{12}{18} = \frac{6}{9}$

4. The figure is divided into sixteenths.
   12 sixteenths are shaded.

   Group each 4 sixteenths.
   The shaded area becomes **3 fourths.**

   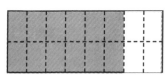
   $\frac{12}{16} = \frac{3}{4}$

5. The figure is divided into twentieths.
   15 twentieths are shaded.

   Group each 5 twentieths.
   The shaded area becomes **3 fourths.**

   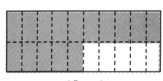
   $\frac{15}{20} = \frac{3}{4}$

6. Group as many units as you can, and then write the fraction you obtain:

   a. $\frac{20}{30} = \frac{2}{3}$ b. $\frac{20}{48} = \frac{5}{12}$ c. $\frac{18}{27} = \frac{2}{3}$

   d. $\frac{8}{10} = \frac{4}{5}$ e. $\frac{5}{100} = \frac{1}{20}$ f. $\frac{75}{1000} = \frac{3}{40}$

   g. $\frac{42}{70} = \frac{3}{5}$ h. $\frac{45}{60} = \frac{3}{4}$ i. $\frac{48}{72} = \frac{2}{3}$

© Copyright by L. George Saad   **Level 15**

3 EXPRESSING A DECIMAL AS A COMMON FRACTION AND VICE VERSA

- You know that .8 or 0.8 may be written $\frac{8}{10}$.
  You also know that $\frac{8}{10}$ may be changed into $\frac{4}{5}$.

  $.8 = \frac{8}{10} = \frac{4}{5}$

- You know that .75 or 0.75 may be written $\frac{75}{100}$.
  You also know that $\frac{75}{100} = \frac{15}{20} = \frac{3}{4}$.

  $.75 = \frac{75}{100} = \frac{15}{20} = \frac{3}{4}$

- You know that .025 or 0.025 may be written $\frac{25}{1000}$.
  You also know that $\frac{25}{1000} = \frac{5}{200} = \frac{1}{40}$.

  $.025 = \frac{25}{1000} = \frac{5}{200} = \frac{1}{40}$

In these examples, we have expressed each decimal fraction as a fraction with a numerator and denominator, and then changed the fraction into the largest unit.

EXERCISES

1. Express as a fraction in the largest unit.

   a. $0.5 = \frac{5}{10} = \frac{1}{2}$

   b. $0.05 = \frac{5}{100} = \frac{1}{20}$

   c. $0.005 = \frac{5}{1000} = \frac{1}{200}$

   d. $0.0005 = \frac{5}{10000} = \frac{1}{2000}$

   e. $0.2 = \frac{2}{10} = \frac{1}{5}$

   f. $0.002 = \frac{2}{1000} = \frac{1}{500}$

   g. $0.6 = \frac{6}{10} = \frac{3}{5}$

   h. $0.25 = \frac{25}{100} = \frac{1}{4}$

   i. $0.125 = \frac{125}{1000} = \frac{5}{40} = \frac{1}{8}$

   j. $0.875 = \frac{875}{1000} = \frac{7}{8}$

   k. $0.625 = \frac{625}{1000} = \frac{5}{8}$

   l. $0.3125 = \frac{3125}{10000} = \frac{125}{400} = \frac{5}{16}$

2. Express the sum of .06 and 0.0025 as a fraction in the largest unit.

   $0.06 + 0.0025 = 0.0625 = \frac{625}{10000} = \frac{1}{16}$

3. Express the difference between 12.7 and 12.675 as a fraction in the largest unit.

   $12.700 - 12.675 = 0.025 = \frac{25}{1000} = \frac{1}{40}$

© Copyright by L. George Saad

EXPRESSING A DECIMAL AS A COMMON FRACTION AND VICE VERSA

Example 1.
   Change $\frac{1}{2}$ into a decimal fraction.
Discussion:
   To change $\frac{1}{2}$ into a decimal fraction we have to
   change it into tenths, or hundredths, or thousandths. $\frac{1}{2} = \frac{5}{10} = 0.5$

Example 2.
   Change $\frac{1}{4}$ into a decimal fraction.
Discussion:
   You cannot change $\frac{1}{4}$ into tenths, but you can
   change it into hundredths. $\frac{1}{4} = \frac{25}{100} = .25$

Example 3.
   Change $\frac{1}{8}$ into a decimal fraction.
Discussion:
   You cannot change $\frac{1}{8}$ into tenths or hundredths,
   but you can change it into thousandths. $\frac{1}{8} = \frac{125}{1000} = .125$

EXERCISES

1. Change into decimal fractions

   a. $\frac{1}{5} = \frac{2}{10} = \textbf{.2}$ b. $\frac{3}{5} = \frac{6}{10} = \textbf{.6}$

   c. $\frac{3}{4} = \frac{75}{100} = \textbf{.75}$ d. $\frac{1}{50} = \frac{2}{100} = \textbf{.02}$

   e. $\frac{3}{50} = \frac{6}{100} = \textbf{.06}$ f. $\frac{37}{50} = \frac{74}{100} = \textbf{.74}$

   g. $\frac{3}{25} = \frac{12}{100} = \textbf{.12}$ h. $\frac{6}{25} = \frac{24}{100} = \textbf{.24}$

   i. $\frac{1}{20} = \frac{5}{100} = \textbf{.05}$ j. $\frac{3}{20} = \frac{15}{100} = \textbf{.15}$

2. Add 1.391 to $\frac{3}{4}$

$$1.391 + 0.750 = 2.141$$

3. Subtract $\frac{4}{5}$ from 0.912

$$0.912 - 0.800 = 0.112$$

© Copyright by L. George Saad   **Level 15**

4 COMPARING FRACTIONS OF DIFFERENT UNITS

Example 1.
   Which is larger $\frac{5}{6}$ or $\frac{3}{6}$?
Discussion:
   The answer is obvious. 5 is larger than 3.
   Thus, 5 sixths is larger than 3 sixths. $\frac{5}{6}$ is larger than $\frac{3}{6}$.

Example 2.
   Which is larger $\frac{1}{2}$ or $\frac{1}{3}$?
Discussion:
   The answer is also obvious.
   If we divide a whole into 3 equal parts, each part will be smaller
   than that if we divide the whole into 2 equal parts. $\frac{1}{2}$ is larger than $\frac{1}{3}$.

Example 3.
   Which is larger $\frac{3}{4}$ or $\frac{11}{12}$?
Discussion:
   • We cannot compare because one fraction is in fourths and
     the other is in twelfths. But, we can change $\frac{3}{4}$ into twelfths. $\frac{3}{4} = \frac{9}{12}$
   • Now we can compare $\frac{9}{12}$ and $\frac{11}{12}$.
     $\frac{11}{12}$ is larger than $\frac{9}{12}$ $\frac{11}{12}$ is larger than $\frac{3}{4}$.

Example 4.
   Which is larger $\frac{2}{3}$ or $\frac{4}{5}$?
Discussion:
   One fraction is in thirds and the other is in fifths.
   We do not have any base to use in comparing the two fractions.

   • Can we change the two fractions into the same fractional unit?
     $\frac{2}{3} = \frac{4}{6} = \frac{6}{9} = \frac{8}{12} = \frac{10}{15} = \frac{12}{18} = \frac{14}{21}$
     $\frac{4}{5} = \frac{8}{10} = \frac{12}{15} = \frac{16}{20} = \frac{20}{25} = \frac{24}{30}$

   • It is clear that the two fractions may be changed into fifteenths.
     $\frac{2}{3} = \frac{10}{15}$ and $\frac{4}{5} = \frac{12}{15}$

   • Now we can compare the two fractions.
     $\frac{12}{15}$ is larger than $\frac{10}{15}$, so $\frac{4}{5}$ is larger than $\frac{2}{3}$

APPLICATIONS

1. a. Complete the following statement:
      We cannot compare $\frac{2}{3}$ and $\frac{5}{6}$ unless __we have the same fractional unit__.

   b. To compare $\frac{3}{4}$ and $\frac{2}{5}$, John changes $\frac{3}{4}$ into $\frac{30}{40}$ and $\frac{2}{5}$ into $\frac{16}{40}$.
      Is it correct to do so? __Yes__
      Why? __He has the same fractional unit.__

2. Arrange the fractions in descending order:

   a. $\frac{1}{5}$, $\frac{1}{8}$, $\frac{1}{7}$

      $\underline{\frac{1}{5} , \frac{1}{7} , \frac{1}{8}}$

   b. $\frac{5}{7}$, $\frac{5}{11}$, $\frac{5}{8}$

      $\underline{\frac{5}{7} , \frac{5}{8} , \frac{5}{11}}$

3. Arrange the fractions in ascending order:

   a. $\frac{2}{3}$, $\frac{5}{8}$, $\frac{7}{12}$

      $\frac{2}{3} = \frac{16}{24}$, $\frac{5}{8} = \frac{15}{24}$, $\frac{7}{12} = \frac{14}{24}$

      $\underline{\frac{7}{12} , \frac{5}{8} , \frac{2}{3}}$

   b. $\frac{3}{4}$, $\frac{5}{6}$, $\frac{7}{9}$

      $\frac{3}{4} = \frac{27}{36}$ $\frac{5}{6} = \frac{30}{36}$ $\frac{7}{9} = \frac{28}{36}$

      $\underline{\frac{3}{4} , \frac{7}{9} , \frac{5}{6}}$

4. Which is larger: 0.123 or $\frac{1}{8}$?

   $\frac{1}{8} = 0.125$ 0.125 is larger than 0.123

   $\frac{1}{8}$ is larger than 0.123

5. Which is smaller: $\frac{5}{7}$ or 0.75?

   $\frac{5}{7} = \frac{20}{28}$ $0.75 = \frac{75}{100} = \frac{3}{4} = \frac{21}{28}$

   $\frac{5}{7}$ is smaller than $\frac{3}{4}$

6. Dan covers 59 miles on 4 gallons of gas, and Tom covers 44 miles on 3 gallons. Whose car is better on gas?

   Dan: $59 \div 4 = 14\frac{3}{4} = 14\frac{9}{12}$ miles per gallon

   Tom: $44 \div 3 = 14\frac{2}{3} = 14\frac{8}{12}$ miles per gallon

   Dan's car is better on gas.

7. Ann bought 5 yards of material for $18. Mary bought 8 yard of material for $29. Who had a better deal?

   Ann: $\$18 \div 5 = \$3\frac{3}{5} = \$3\frac{24}{40}$ per yard

   Mary: $\$29 \div 8 = \$3\frac{5}{8} = \$3\frac{25}{40}$ per yard

   Ann had a better deal.

© Copyright by L. George Saad   **Level 15**

5 DIVIDING A NUMBER BY A LARGER NUMBER

Example 1.

a. Janet bought material which cost $4 a yard.

She paid $3.

How much material did Janet buy?

Discussion:

• You may answer the question in the following way:

$4 is the cost of 1 yd.

$1 is the cost of $\frac{1}{4}$ yd.

$3 is the cost of $\frac{3}{4}$ of a yard.

• You also may answer the question in one step.

Find how many 4's are in 3, which calls for

the division: $3 \div 4$ $3 \div 4 = \frac{3}{4}$

---

b. Janet bought 4 yards of material.

She paid $3.

How much did one yard of the material cost?

Discussion:

• You may answer the question in the following way:

4 yds. cost $3.

1 yd. cost $\frac{3}{4}$

• You also may answer the question in one step.

Divide $3 into 4 equal amounts, which calls

for the division $3 \div 4$. $3 \div 4 = \frac{3}{4}$

Example 2.

a. How many 5 wholes are in 3 wholes?	b. Divide 3 wholes into 5 equal portions.
Discussion:	What part of one whole do you get?
You make groups of 5, which calls for	Discussion:
the division $3 \div 5$	You divide each one whole into fifths,
You can only make $\frac{3}{5}$ of one group.	and then take one fifth of each whole.
Thus, $3 \div 5 = \frac{3}{5}$	Thus $3 \div 5 = \frac{3}{5}$

NOTE:

A division expression is sometimes written in fractional form, in which

the numerator is the dividend and the denominator is the divisor.

© Copyright by L. George Saad

APPLICATIONS

Use division to solve the following problems:

1. You covered 18 miles in 30 minutes.
   How many miles did you cover per minute?

   $$18 \div 30 = \frac{18}{30} = \frac{9}{15} = \frac{3}{5}$$

2. You covered 30 miles, at a speed of
   50 miles per hour. How many hours did you drive?

   $$30 \div 50 = \frac{30}{50} = \frac{3}{5}$$

3. 8 jars of jam of the same size weigh 6 lbs.
   How many pounds is the weight of each jar?

   $$6 \div 8 = \frac{6}{8} = \frac{3}{4}$$

4. 16 ounces of jam are put into a 28-ounce jar.
   How much of the jar is filled with jam?

   $$16 \div 28 = \frac{16}{28} = \frac{4}{7}$$

5. Approximately 91 centimeters are equivalent
   to 36 inches.
   How many inches are equivalent to one centimeter?

   $$36 \div 91 = \frac{36}{91}$$

6. Approximately 100 kilograms are equivalent
   to 220 pounds.
   How many kilograms are equivalent to one pound?

   $$100 \div 220 = \frac{100}{220} = \frac{5}{11}$$

7. a. A dairy farmer poured 30 gallons of
      milk in a 40-gallon tank.
      How much of the tank is filled with milk?

      $$30 \div 40 = \frac{30}{40} = \frac{3}{4}$$

   b. A dairy farmer divided 30 gallons of
      milk equally in 40 containers.
      How much milk was in each container?

      $$30 \div 40 = \frac{30}{40} = \frac{3}{4} \text{ gallon}$$

8. a. You divided 18 yards of string into 20 equal parts.
      How long was each part?

      $$18 \div 20 = \frac{18}{20} = \frac{9}{10} \text{ yard}$$

   b. You have 18 yards of string.
      You need 20 yards to fly a kite.
      How much of what you need do you have?

      $$18 \div 20 = \frac{18}{20} = \frac{9}{10}$$

© Copyright by L. George Saad   **Level 15**

6 CHANGING A FRACTION INTO A DECIMAL

Example 1.

Change $\frac{3}{8}$ into a decimal fraction.

$$\begin{array}{r} 0.375 \\ 8)\overline{3.000} \end{array}$$

Discussion:

$\frac{3}{8}$ may mean, "How many eights are in 3?"

which is the same as $3 \div 8$.

To the right 3 is divided by 8.　　　$\frac{3}{8} = 0.375$

Example 2.

Change $\frac{7}{16}$ into a decimal fraction.

$$\begin{array}{r} 0.4375 \\ 16)\overline{7.0000} \\ \underline{6\,4} \\ 60 \\ \underline{48} \\ 120 \\ \underline{112} \\ 80 \\ \underline{80} \\ 0 \end{array}$$

Discussion:

Complete the division to the right.　　　$\frac{7}{16} = \mathbf{0.4375}$

Example 3.

Which is larger $\frac{5}{8}$ or 0.617?

Discussion:

$$\begin{array}{r} 0.625 \\ 8)\overline{5.000} \end{array}$$

- We cannot compare unless we have the two fractions in the same fractional unit.
- It is obvious that it is easier to work with decimal fractions.
- Express $\frac{5}{8}$ as a decimal fraction　　　$\frac{5}{8} = \mathbf{0.625}$
- Now you are able to compare.　　　$\frac{5}{8}$ is larger than 0.617

Example 4.

Find the sum of $\frac{3}{8}$ and 0.084

$$\begin{array}{r} 0.375 \\ 8)\overline{3.000} \end{array}$$

Discussion:

It is obvious that it is better to change $\frac{3}{8}$ into a
decimal fraction which you then add to 0.084

$$\frac{3}{8} = 0.375$$

$$\frac{3}{8} + 0.084 = 0.375 + 0.084 = 0.459$$

Level 15　　　　　　　　　　　　　　　　　　　© Copyright by L. George Saad

APPLICATIONS

1. Change into a decimal fraction.

a. $\frac{1}{8} = 0.125$

$$8)\overline{1.000} \quad \begin{array}{r} 0.125 \\ \underline{8} \\ 20 \\ \underline{16} \\ 40 \\ \underline{40} \\ 0 \end{array}$$

b. $\frac{7}{8} = 0.875$

$$8)\overline{7.000} \quad \begin{array}{r} 0.875 \\ \underline{6\ 4} \\ 60 \\ \underline{56} \\ 40 \\ \underline{40} \\ 0 \end{array}$$

c. $\frac{5}{8} = 0.625$

$$8)\overline{5.000} \quad \begin{array}{r} 0.625 \\ \underline{4\ 8} \\ 20 \\ \underline{16} \\ 40 \\ \underline{40} \\ 0 \end{array}$$

d. $\frac{3}{16} = 0.1875$

$$16)\overline{3.0000} \quad \begin{array}{r} 0.1875 \\ \underline{1\ 6} \\ 140 \\ \underline{128} \\ 120 \\ \underline{112} \\ 80 \\ \underline{80} \end{array}$$

e. $\frac{7}{16} = 0.4375$

$$16)\overline{7.0000} \quad \begin{array}{r} 0.4375 \\ \underline{6\ 4} \\ 60 \\ \underline{48} \\ 120 \\ \underline{112} \\ 80 \\ \underline{80} \end{array}$$

f. $\frac{9}{16} = 0.5625$

$$16)\overline{9.0000} \quad \begin{array}{r} 0.5625 \\ \underline{8\ 0} \\ 1\ 00 \\ \underline{96} \\ 40 \\ \underline{32} \\ 80 \\ \underline{80} \end{array}$$

2. Subtract $\frac{3}{8}$ from 3.026.

$$3.026 - 0.375 = 2.651$$

3. Find the difference between $\frac{5}{8}$ and 0.605.

$$0.625 - 0.605 = 0.020$$

4. Find the sum of $\frac{7}{8}$ and 3.012.

$$0.875 + 3.012 = 3.887$$

5. What number do you subtract from 0.991 for the answer to be equal to $\frac{7}{16}$?

$$0.9910 - 0.4375 = 0.5535$$

6. What number do you add to $\frac{3}{8}$ for the answer to be 0.812

$$0.812 - 0.375 = 0.437$$

© Copyright by L. George Saad

Date _____

7   MATHEMATICAL VOCABULARY

Terms of a fraction.

The numerator and denominator of a fraction are called the terms of a fraction.

The terms of $\frac{2}{3}$ are 2 and 3.   The terms of $\frac{7}{8}$ are 7 and 8.

The terms of $\frac{9}{10}$ are __9__ and __10__   The terms of $\frac{37}{100}$ are __37__ and __100__

- Changing a fraction into smaller fractional units, as shown in the examples to the right, is called changing into higher terms.

$$\frac{2}{3} = \frac{4}{6}$$
$$\frac{5}{7} = \frac{20}{28}$$

- Changing a fraction into larger fractional units, as shown in the examples to the right, is called changing into lower terms.

$$\frac{10}{20} = \frac{2}{4}$$
$$\frac{24}{36} = \frac{4}{6}$$

- If a fraction is changed into the largest possible fractional unit, as shown to the right, the terms are the lowest possible.

$$\frac{15}{75} = \frac{3}{15} = \frac{1}{5}$$
$$\frac{12}{18} = \frac{6}{9} = \frac{2}{3}$$
$$\frac{42}{56} = \frac{6}{8} = \frac{3}{4}$$

Simplifying a fraction

- When a fraction is changed to the largest possible fractional unit, as in the examples to the right, the fraction is in simplest form.

$$\frac{35}{45} = \frac{7}{9}$$
$$\frac{36}{54} = \frac{6}{9} = \frac{2}{3}$$
$$\frac{63}{84} = \frac{9}{12} = \frac{3}{4}$$

APPLICATIONS

1. a. What are the terms of the fraction $\frac{6}{7}$?   __6 and 7__

   b. What are the terms of the fraction $\frac{x}{9}$?   __x and 9__

2. a. Write a fraction whose terms are 5 and 7. $\frac{5}{7}$, $\frac{7}{5}$

   b. Write a fraction whose terms are x and y. $\frac{y}{x}$, $\frac{x}{y}$

3. Simplify each fraction into its lowest terms.

   a. $\frac{3}{6} = \frac{1}{2}$ b. $\frac{4}{8} = \frac{1}{2}$ c. $\frac{5}{15} = \frac{1}{3}$ d. $\frac{12}{24} = \frac{1}{2}$

   e. $\frac{4}{6} = \frac{2}{3}$ f. $\frac{8}{12} = \frac{2}{3}$ g. $\frac{15}{20} = \frac{3}{4}$ h. $\frac{32}{48} = \frac{2}{3}$

    © Copyright by L. George Saad

4. Express each fraction in higher terms:

   a. $\frac{3}{5} = \frac{6}{10}$ or $\frac{9}{15}$ or $\frac{12}{20}$ or...

   b. $\frac{6}{7} = \frac{12}{14}$ or $\frac{18}{21}$ or $\frac{24}{28}$ or...

   c. $\frac{14}{15} = \frac{28}{30}$ or $\frac{42}{45}$ or $\frac{56}{60}$ or...

   d. $\frac{12}{19} = \frac{24}{38}$ or $\frac{36}{57}$ or $\frac{48}{76}$ or...

   e. $\frac{27}{36} = \frac{54}{72}$ or $\frac{81}{108}$ or $\frac{108}{144}$ or...

   f. $\frac{39}{84} = \frac{78}{168}$ or $\frac{117}{252}$ or $\frac{156}{336}$ or...

5. a. $\frac{X}{8}$ is a proper fraction in simplest form.
   What values may X take?   __1, 3, 5, 7__

   b. $\frac{6}{Y}$ is a proper fraction in simplest form.
   If Y is less than 15, what values may Y take?   __7. 11. 13__

6. $\frac{3}{7}$ is the simplest form of a fraction.

   a. If the numerator is changed to 21, what is
   the denominator of the new fraction?   __49__

   b. If the denominator is changed to 21, what is
   the numerator of the new fraction?   __9__

7. If a fraction is simplified into $\frac{1}{3}$, which statement
   describes the original fraction?

   a. The denominator is 2 more than the numerator.   __No__

   b. The denominator is 3 times the numerator.   __Yes__

8. Show how you change the fraction into the simplest form:

   a. To simplify $\frac{35}{45}$, you __divide 35 and 45 by 5.__

   b. To simplify $\frac{24}{36}$, you __divide 24 and 36 by 12.__

   c. To simplify $\frac{75}{100}$, you __divide 75 and 100 by 25.__

   d. To simplify $\frac{30}{75}$, you __divide 30 and 75 by 15.__

9. a. 13 is the numerator of an improper fraction in its
   simplest form. What number is the denominator?   __2, 3, 4,...12__

   b. 13 is the denominator of a proper fraction in its
   simplest form. What number is the numerator?   __1, 2, 3,...12__

© Copyright by L. George Saad   **Level 15**

Date _____

Equivalent Fractions

Fractions which have the same value are called equivalent fractions.

Example 1.   Example 2.

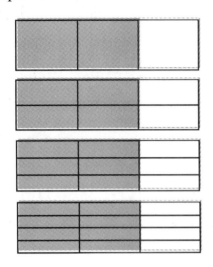   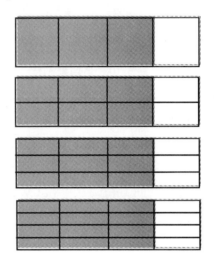

$\frac{2}{3}$ of a figure has the same value $\frac{3}{4}$ of a figure has the same value

as $\frac{4}{6}$, $\frac{6}{9}$, and $\frac{8}{12}$ of the figure.   as $\frac{6}{8}$, $\frac{9}{12}$, and $\frac{12}{16}$ of the figure.

$\frac{2}{3}$, $\frac{4}{6}$, $\frac{6}{9}$, and $\frac{8}{12}$ are equivalent fractions. $\frac{3}{4}$, $\frac{6}{8}$, $\frac{9}{12}$, and $\frac{12}{16}$ are equivalent fractions.

Example 3.

Find out whether $\frac{10}{14}$ and $\frac{35}{49}$ are equivalent.

Discussion:

The two fractions have to be simplified to lowest terms.

$\frac{10}{14}$ is simplified into $\frac{5}{7}$

$\frac{35}{49}$ is simplified into $\frac{5}{7}$

Both fractions have the same value. $\frac{10}{14}$ and $\frac{35}{49}$ are equivalent fractions.

Equivalent decimal fractions

$\frac{30}{100}$, $\frac{300}{1000}$ may be simplified into $\frac{3}{10}$. $\frac{3}{10}$, $\frac{30}{100}$, and $\frac{300}{1000}$ are equivalent.

Writing the fractions as decimals: 0.3, 0.30, and 0.300 are equivalent.

Examples:

0.8 = 0.80 = 0.800 = 0.8000

3.09 = 3.090 = 3.0900 = 3.09000

© Copyright by L. George Saad

APPLICATIONS

1. Write four fractions equivalent to $\frac{2}{3}$.

   $\frac{4}{6}$, $\frac{6}{9}$, $\frac{8}{12}$, $\frac{10}{15}$, $\frac{12}{18}$, $\frac{14}{21}$, $\frac{16}{24}$, $\frac{18}{27}$, $\frac{20}{30}$ ...etc.

2. Which of the following fractions is equivalent to $\frac{3}{4}$?

   a. $\frac{15}{20}$ b. $\frac{5}{6}$ c. $\frac{2}{3}$ d. $\frac{53}{54}$ e. $\frac{27}{36}$ __a, e__

3. Which fractions are equivalent?

   a. $\frac{21}{35}$ b. $\frac{12}{20}$ c. $\frac{8}{10}$ d. $\frac{9}{15}$ e. $\frac{23}{25}$ __a, b, d__

4. Which fractions are equivalent?

   a. $\frac{3}{4}$ b. $\frac{45}{60}$ c. $\frac{24}{36}$ d. $\frac{24}{32}$ e. $\frac{18}{24}$ __a, b, d, e__

5. a. Write a fraction equivalent to 0.5

   b. Write a fraction equivalent to 0.05

   $\frac{5}{10} = \frac{1}{2} = \frac{3}{6} = \frac{2}{4} = \frac{4}{8} = \ldots$

   $\frac{5}{100} = \frac{1}{20} = \frac{10}{200} = \frac{2}{40} = \ldots$

6. Which of the following fractions is equivalent to .9?

   a. 0.90 b. 0.99 c. 0.909 d. 0.009 e. 0.900 __a, e__

7. The following decimals are equivalent: 0.70, 0.7, 0.7000.

   Why? $.7 = \frac{7}{10}$ $.70 = \frac{70}{100} = \frac{7}{10}$ $.700 = \frac{700}{1000} = \frac{7}{10}$

8. Find out whether $\frac{54}{72}$ and $\frac{3}{4}$ are equivalent.

   $\frac{54}{72} = \frac{6}{8} = \frac{3}{4}$ They are equivalent.

9. Find out whether $\frac{13}{48}$ and $\frac{15}{40}$ are equivalent.

   $\frac{13}{48}$ is in simplest form. $\frac{15}{40} = \frac{3}{8}$ They are not equivalent.

10. Find out whether $\frac{21}{27}$ and $\frac{56}{72}$ are equivalent.

   $\frac{21}{27} = \frac{7}{9}$ $\frac{56}{72} = \frac{7}{9}$ They are equivalent.

© Copyright by L. George Saad

Level 15

UNIT A TEST

1. Show that the equation $\frac{1}{2} = \frac{35}{70}$ is correct.
   Each $\frac{1}{2}$ is divided into 35 equal parts.
   The whole becomes 70 equal parts.

2. Write the missing number:

   a. $\frac{3}{8} = \frac{9}{24}$ b. $\frac{3}{4} = \frac{30}{40}$ c. $\frac{7}{9} = \frac{28}{36}$

   d. $\frac{3}{5} = \frac{15}{25}$ e. $\frac{2}{7} = \frac{28}{98}$ f. $\frac{4}{9} = \frac{52}{117}$

3. Show that the equation $\frac{35}{40} = \frac{7}{8}$ is correct.
   Group each 5 fortieths to get eighths.
   $35 \div 5 = 7$

4. Write the missing number:

   a. $\frac{14}{35} = \frac{2}{5}$ b. $\frac{12}{36} = \frac{4}{12}$ c. $\frac{12}{18} = \frac{2}{3}$

   d. $\frac{24}{36} = \frac{4}{6}$ e. $\frac{18}{28} = \frac{9}{14}$ f. $\frac{24}{40} = \frac{3}{5}$

5. $0.6 = \frac{3}{5}$ Why? $0.6 = \frac{6}{10} = \frac{3}{5}$

6. Express as a fraction:

   a. $0.8 = \frac{8}{10} = \frac{4}{5}$ b. $0.25 = \frac{25}{100} = \frac{1}{4}$

   c. $0.05 = \frac{5}{100} = \frac{1}{20}$ d. $0.075 = \frac{75}{1000} = \frac{3}{40}$

7. $\frac{3}{4} = 0.75$.   Why?   4 fourths become 100 hundredths.
   $\frac{3}{4} = \frac{75}{100}$ 1 fourth becomes 25 hundredths.
   3 fourths become 75 hundredths.

8. Express as a decimal:

   a. $\frac{1}{2} = \frac{5}{10} = 0.5$ b. $\frac{7}{20} = \frac{35}{100} = 0.35$

   c. $\frac{9}{50} = \frac{18}{100} = 0.18$ d. $\frac{2}{25} = \frac{8}{100} = 0.08$

9. a. Complete the following statement: "We cannot compare $\frac{5}{6}$ and $\frac{7}{8}$ unless we have the same fractional unit.

    b. Compare $\frac{5}{8}$ and $\frac{7}{10}$.
    $\frac{5}{8} = \frac{25}{40}$, $\frac{7}{10} = \frac{28}{40}$ $\frac{5}{8}$ is less than $\frac{7}{10}$.

10. You had a pipe 12 feet long.
    You cut it into 18 equal pieces.
    How long is each piece? $12 \div 18 = \frac{12}{18} = \frac{2}{3}$ ft.

11. a. Change $\frac{7}{16}$ into a decimal fraction.

    $\frac{7}{16} = 7 \div 16 = 0.4375$

    b. Add $\frac{7}{16}$ to 0.73

    $0.4375 + 0.0730 = 0.5105$

    $\begin{array}{r} .4375 \\ 16)\overline{7.0000} \\ \underline{6\ 4} \\ 60 \\ \underline{48} \\ 120 \\ \underline{112} \\ 80 \\ \underline{80} \end{array}$

12. What are the terms of the fraction $\frac{7}{8}$?

    7 and 8

13. How do you simplify the fraction $\frac{30}{50}$?

    Divide 30 and 50 by 10.

14. Simplify each fraction to its lowest terms:

    a. $\frac{4}{8} = \frac{1}{2}$ b. $\frac{15}{18} = \frac{5}{6}$

    c. $\frac{24}{36} = \frac{2}{3}$ d. $\frac{45}{60} = \frac{3}{4}$

15. 6 is the denominator of a proper fraction in its
    lowest terms.
    What number may be the numerator?   1 or 5

16. Which of the following fractions is equivalent to $\frac{8}{10}$?

    a. $\frac{12}{15}$ b. $\frac{12}{14}$ c. $\frac{28}{35}$ d. $\frac{80}{100}$ a, c, d

17. Find out whether $\frac{24}{36}$ and $\frac{16}{24}$ are equivalent fractions.

    $\frac{24}{36} = \frac{2}{3}$ $\frac{16}{24} = \frac{2}{3}$ They are equivalent.

© Copyright by L. George Saad

8 ADDING FRACTIONS OF DIFFERENT UNITS

Example 1.

Jane bought $\frac{5}{8}$ yd. of material but she needed $\frac{1}{4}$ yd. more to make a dress.
How much material did she use to make the dress?

Discussion:

It is obvious that we have to add $\frac{5}{8}$ and $\frac{1}{4}$.

The two fractions are in different units, eighths and fourths.

To add the two fractions, they must be in the same unit.

It is possible to change the fourths into eighths.

We know that $\frac{1}{4} = \frac{2}{8}$ $\frac{5}{8} + \frac{1}{4} = \frac{5}{8} + \frac{2}{8} = \frac{7}{8}$

Example 2.

Add: $\frac{2}{3} + \frac{4}{5}$

Discussion:

The two fractions are in different units.

We have to convert the two fractions into the same fractional unit.

The two fractions may be changed into fifteenths, or thirtieths, or forty-fifths, or …

It is easier, of course, to change them into fifteenths.

$\frac{2}{3} = \frac{10}{15}$ $\frac{4}{5} = \frac{12}{15}$ $\frac{2}{3} + \frac{4}{5} = \frac{10}{15} + \frac{12}{15} = \frac{22}{15} = 1\frac{7}{15}$

You can do the work vertically
as shown to the right.

$$\frac{2}{3} = \frac{10}{15}$$
$$+ \frac{4}{5} = \frac{12}{15}$$
$$\overline{\quad\quad\quad}$$
$$\frac{22}{15} = 1\frac{7}{15}$$

Example 3.

Add: $9\frac{3}{8} + 7\frac{5}{6}$

Discussion:

We have to convert the fractions $\frac{3}{8}$ and $\frac{5}{6}$ into
the same fractional unit which may be twenty-
fourths or forty-eighths or seventy-seconds.

It is easier, of course, to convert into twenty-fourths.

$$9\frac{3}{8} = 9\frac{9}{24}$$
$$+ 7\frac{5}{6} = 7\frac{20}{24}$$
$$\overline{\quad\quad\quad}$$
$$16\frac{29}{24} = 17\frac{5}{24}$$

Add:

1. $\frac{1}{4} + \frac{1}{8} = \frac{2}{8} + \frac{1}{8} = \frac{3}{8}$

2. $\frac{2}{3} + \frac{1}{6} = \frac{4}{6} + \frac{1}{6} = \frac{5}{6}$

3. $\frac{3}{12} + \frac{5}{6} = \frac{3}{12} + \frac{10}{12} = \frac{13}{12} = 1\frac{1}{12}$

4. $\frac{1}{2} + \frac{1}{3} = \frac{3}{6} + \frac{2}{6} = \frac{5}{6}$

5. $\frac{1}{4} + \frac{1}{5} = \frac{5}{20} + \frac{4}{20} = \frac{9}{20}$

6. $\frac{1}{7} + \frac{1}{6} = \frac{6}{42} + \frac{7}{42} = \frac{13}{42}$

7. $\frac{1}{4} + \frac{1}{6} = \frac{3}{12} + \frac{2}{12} = \frac{5}{12}$

8. $\frac{1}{8} + \frac{1}{10} = \frac{5}{40} + \frac{4}{40} = \frac{9}{40}$

9. $3\frac{1}{4} + \frac{5}{8} = \frac{2}{8}3\frac{5}{8} + \frac{7}{8}3$

10. $9\frac{5}{6} + 1\frac{3}{4} = 9\frac{10}{12} + 1\frac{9}{12} = 10\frac{19}{12} = 11\frac{7}{12}$

11. $7\frac{7}{9} + 5\frac{5}{6} = 7\frac{14}{18} + 5\frac{15}{18} = 12\frac{29}{18} = 13\frac{11}{18}$

12. $2\frac{7}{8} + 4\frac{2}{3} = 2\frac{21}{24} + 4\frac{16}{24} = 6\frac{37}{24} = 7\frac{13}{24}$

13. $1\frac{5}{6} + 2\frac{2}{3} + 7\frac{3}{4} = 1\frac{10}{12} + 2\frac{8}{12} + 7\frac{9}{12} = 10\frac{27}{12} = 12\frac{3}{12} = 12\frac{1}{4}$

14. $\begin{aligned} 3\frac{1}{2} &= 3\frac{2}{4} \\ + \quad \frac{3}{4} &= \quad \frac{3}{4} \\ \hline 3\frac{5}{4} &= 4\frac{1}{4} \end{aligned}$	15. $\begin{aligned} 6\frac{3}{4} &= 6\frac{6}{8} \\ + 2\frac{5}{8} &= 2\frac{5}{8} \\ \hline 8\frac{11}{8} &= 9\frac{3}{8} \end{aligned}$	16. $\begin{aligned} 5\frac{2}{3} &= 5\frac{6}{9} \\ + \quad \frac{5}{9} &= \quad \frac{5}{9} \\ \hline 5\frac{11}{9} &= 6\frac{2}{9} \end{aligned}$
17. $\begin{aligned} 9\frac{1}{2} &= 9\frac{5}{10} \\ + 6\frac{3}{5} &= 6\frac{6}{10} \\ \hline 15\frac{11}{10} &= 16\frac{1}{10} \end{aligned}$	18. $\begin{aligned} 7\frac{3}{8} &= 7\frac{9}{24} \\ + 2\frac{5}{6} &= 2\frac{20}{24} \\ \hline 9\frac{29}{24} &= 10\frac{5}{24} \end{aligned}$	19. $\begin{aligned} 3\frac{5}{9} &= 3\frac{10}{18} \\ + 4\frac{5}{6} &= 4\frac{15}{18} \\ \hline 7\frac{25}{18} &= 8\frac{7}{18} \end{aligned}$
20. $\begin{aligned} 10\frac{1}{2} &= 10\frac{3}{6} \\ \frac{2}{3} &= \frac{4}{6} \\ + 6\frac{5}{6} &= 6\frac{5}{6} \\ \hline 16\frac{12}{6} &= 18 \end{aligned}$	21. $\begin{aligned} \frac{7}{15} &= \frac{7}{15} \\ 2\frac{1}{3} &= 2\frac{5}{15} \\ + 6\frac{2}{5} &= 6\frac{6}{15} \\ \hline 8\frac{18}{15} &= 9\frac{1}{5} \end{aligned}$	22. $\begin{aligned} \frac{3}{4} &= \frac{9}{12} \\ \frac{2}{3} &= \frac{8}{12} \\ + 8\frac{5}{6} &= 8\frac{10}{12} \\ \hline 8\frac{27}{12} &= 10\frac{1}{4} \end{aligned}$

© Copyright by L. George Saad

Level 15

Date _____

9 SUBTRACTING FRACTIONS OF DIFFERENT UNITS

Example 1.

You have a board $\frac{2}{3}$ yd. long.

You cut a piece $\frac{1}{4}$ yd. long.

How long is the piece left?

Discussion:

It is obvious that we have to subtract: $\frac{2}{3} - \frac{1}{4}$

We can't subtract unless we have the two fractions in the same fractional unit.

Which fractional unit would you chose? __twelfths__

$$\frac{2}{3} = \frac{8}{12} \qquad \frac{1}{4} = \frac{3}{12} \qquad\qquad \frac{2}{3} - \frac{1}{4} = \frac{8}{12} - \frac{3}{12} = \frac{5}{12}$$

Example 2.

Subtract: $7\frac{3}{4} - \frac{5}{8}$

Discussion:

To subtract a fraction from another, they have to be in the same fractional unit.

We start by changing $\frac{3}{4}$ into $\frac{6}{8}$ $\qquad\qquad 7\frac{3}{4} - \frac{5}{8} = 7\frac{6}{8} - \frac{5}{8} = 7\frac{1}{8}$

Example 3.

Subtract: $9\frac{1}{3} - 2\frac{4}{5}$

Discussion:

We start by converting $\frac{1}{3}$ and $\frac{4}{5}$

into the same fractional unit.

We convert $\frac{1}{3}$ into $\frac{5}{15}$ and $\frac{4}{5}$ into $\frac{12}{15}$

$$9\frac{1}{3} = 9\frac{5}{15} = 8\frac{20}{15}$$
$$-2\frac{4}{5} = 2\frac{12}{15} = 2\frac{12}{15}$$
$$6\frac{8}{15}$$

Example 4.

Subtract: $8\frac{1}{6} - 4\frac{5}{8}$

Discussion:

We first change $\frac{1}{6}$ and $\frac{5}{8}$ into

the same fractional units.

We change $\frac{1}{6}$ into $\frac{4}{24}$ and $\frac{5}{8}$ into $\frac{15}{24}$

$$8\frac{1}{6} = 8\frac{4}{24} = 7\frac{28}{24}$$
$$-4\frac{5}{8} = 4\frac{15}{24} = 4\frac{15}{24}$$
$$3\frac{13}{24}$$

B

© Copyright by L. George Saad

Subtract:

1. $\dfrac{1}{2} - \dfrac{1}{4} = \dfrac{2}{4} - \dfrac{1}{4} = \dfrac{1}{4}$

2. $\dfrac{1}{3} - \dfrac{1}{9} = \dfrac{3}{9} - \dfrac{1}{9} = \dfrac{2}{9}$

3. $\dfrac{1}{3} - \dfrac{1}{5} = \dfrac{5}{15} - \dfrac{3}{15} = \dfrac{2}{15}$

4. $\dfrac{1}{7} - \dfrac{1}{8} = \dfrac{8}{56} - \dfrac{7}{56} = \dfrac{1}{56}$

5. $\dfrac{3}{4} - \dfrac{3}{5} = \dfrac{15}{20} - \dfrac{12}{20} = \dfrac{3}{20}$

6. $\dfrac{6}{7} - \dfrac{3}{8} = \dfrac{48}{56} - \dfrac{21}{56} = \dfrac{27}{56}$

7. $8\dfrac{2}{5} - 3\dfrac{1}{3} = 8\dfrac{6}{15} - 3\dfrac{5}{15} = 5\dfrac{1}{15}$

8. $7\dfrac{1}{2} - 2\dfrac{1}{3} = 7\dfrac{3}{6} - 2\dfrac{2}{6} = 5\dfrac{1}{6}$

9. $4\dfrac{5}{8} - 2\dfrac{2}{3} = 4\dfrac{15}{24} - 2\dfrac{16}{24} = 1\dfrac{23}{24}$

10. $9\dfrac{3}{5} - 1\dfrac{1}{2} = 9\dfrac{6}{10} - 1\dfrac{5}{10} = 8\dfrac{1}{10}$

11. $3\dfrac{1}{5} - 2\dfrac{3}{4} = 3\dfrac{4}{20} - 2\dfrac{15}{20} = \dfrac{9}{20}$

12. $8\dfrac{7}{9} - 3\dfrac{5}{6} = 8\dfrac{14}{18} - 3\dfrac{15}{18} = 4\dfrac{17}{18}$

13. $7\dfrac{2}{3} - 5\dfrac{3}{4} = 7\dfrac{8}{15} - 5\dfrac{9}{12} = 1\dfrac{11}{12}$

14. $6\dfrac{7}{10} - 5\dfrac{5}{8} = 6\dfrac{28}{40} - 5\dfrac{25}{40} = 1\dfrac{3}{40}$

15. $9\dfrac{1}{8} - 3\dfrac{5}{6} = 9\dfrac{3}{24} - 3\dfrac{20}{24} = 5\dfrac{7}{24}$

16. $15\dfrac{3}{4} - 7\dfrac{5}{6} = 15\dfrac{9}{12} - 7\dfrac{10}{12} = 7\dfrac{11}{12}$

17.
$$\begin{array}{r} 9\dfrac{5}{6} = 9\dfrac{20}{24} \\[4pt] -\ 4\dfrac{3}{8} = 4\dfrac{9}{24} \\[2pt] \hline 5\dfrac{11}{24} \end{array}$$

18.
$$\begin{array}{r} 7\dfrac{5}{9} = 7\dfrac{10}{18} = 6\dfrac{28}{18} \\[4pt] -\ 2\dfrac{5}{6} = 2\dfrac{15}{18} = 2\dfrac{15}{28} \\[2pt] \hline 4\dfrac{13}{18} \end{array}$$

19.
$$\begin{array}{r} 10\dfrac{2}{5} = 10\dfrac{8}{20} = 9\dfrac{28}{20} \\[4pt] -\ \dfrac{3}{4} = \dfrac{15}{20} = \dfrac{15}{20} \\[2pt] \hline 9\dfrac{13}{20} \end{array}$$

20.
$$\begin{array}{r} 7\dfrac{3}{8} = 7\dfrac{9}{24} = 6\dfrac{33}{24} \\[4pt] -\ 5\dfrac{5}{6} = 5\dfrac{20}{24} = 5\dfrac{20}{24} \\[2pt] \hline 1\dfrac{13}{24} \end{array}$$

21.
$$\begin{array}{r} 14\dfrac{3}{5} = 14\dfrac{9}{15} = 13\dfrac{24}{15} \\[4pt] -\ 12\dfrac{2}{3} = 12\dfrac{10}{15} = 12\dfrac{10}{15} \\[2pt] \hline 1\dfrac{14}{15} \end{array}$$

22.
$$\begin{array}{r} 18\dfrac{2}{3} = 18\dfrac{8}{12} = 17\dfrac{20}{12} \\[4pt] -\ 6\dfrac{3}{4} = 6\dfrac{9}{12} = 6\dfrac{9}{12} \\[2pt] \hline 11\dfrac{11}{12} \end{array}$$

23.
$$\begin{array}{r} 10\dfrac{5}{8} = 10\dfrac{15}{24} = 9\dfrac{39}{24} \\[4pt] -\ 5\dfrac{5}{6} = 5\dfrac{20}{24} = 5\dfrac{20}{24} \\[2pt] \hline 4\dfrac{19}{24} \end{array}$$

24.
$$\begin{array}{r} 12\dfrac{1}{6} = 12\dfrac{3}{18} = 11\dfrac{21}{18} \\[4pt] -\ 3\dfrac{7}{9} = 3\dfrac{14}{18} = 3\dfrac{14}{18} \\[2pt] \hline 8\dfrac{7}{18} \end{array}$$

25.
$$\begin{array}{r} 14\dfrac{1}{6} = 14\dfrac{2}{12} = 13\dfrac{14}{12} \\[4pt] -\ 9\dfrac{3}{4} = 9\dfrac{9}{12} = 9\dfrac{9}{12} \\[2pt] \hline 4\dfrac{5}{12} \end{array}$$

B

© Copyright by L. George Saad

Level 15

APPLICATIONS

1. Mother bought $6\frac{1}{8}$ lb. of steak in 2 pieces.
   One piece weighed $2\frac{3}{4}$ lb.
   How many pounds did the other piece weigh?

   $$6\frac{1}{8} - 2\frac{3}{4} = 5\frac{9}{8} - 2\frac{5}{8} = 3\frac{3}{8}$$

2. A farmer had a container full of milk.
   When he sold $5\frac{3}{4}$ gallons of milk, $2\frac{1}{2}$
   gallons were left in the container.
   How many gallons of milk did the
   farmer have to start with?

   $$5\frac{3}{4} + 2\frac{1}{2} = 5\frac{3}{4} + 2\frac{2}{4} = 7\frac{5}{4} = 8\frac{1}{4}$$

3. To the right is a picture of a vegetable garden.
   Find the distance around the garden.
   (dimensions are in meters)

   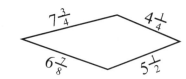

   $$6\frac{7}{8} + 5\frac{4}{8} + 4\frac{2}{8} + 7\frac{6}{8} = 22\frac{19}{8} = 24\frac{3}{8} \text{ meters}$$

4. Dick is $15\frac{1}{4}$ years old.
   Jim is $1\frac{2}{3}$ years older than Dick.
   Fred is $2\frac{3}{4}$ years younger than Jim.
   a. How old is Jim? $15\frac{1}{4} + 1\frac{2}{3} = 15\frac{3}{12} + 1\frac{8}{12} = 16\frac{11}{12} \text{ years}$

   b. How old is Fred? $16\frac{11}{12} - 2\frac{3}{4} = 16\frac{11}{12} - 2\frac{9}{12} = 14\frac{2}{12} = 14\frac{1}{6} \text{ years}$

5. Tom worked $1\frac{3}{4}$ hrs. on Monday,
   $2\frac{1}{2}$ hrs. on Tuesday, and $3\frac{3}{4}$ hrs.
   on Wednesday. How many hours
   did he work on the three days?

   $$1\frac{3}{4} + 2\frac{2}{4} + 3\frac{3}{4} = 6\frac{8}{4} = 8 \text{ hours}$$

© Copyright by L. George Saad

6. Jane baked $3\frac{5}{6}$ dozen cookies for a party. She baked $1\frac{1}{2}$ dozen, then she baked $2\frac{3}{4}$ dozen more. How many dozens did she bake in all?

$$3\frac{5}{6} - 1\frac{1}{2} = 3\frac{5}{6} - 1\frac{3}{6} = 2\frac{2}{6} = 2\frac{1}{3}$$
$$2\frac{1}{3} + 2\frac{3}{4} = 2\frac{4}{12} + 2\frac{9}{12} = 5\frac{1}{12}$$

7. Mark had a bag containing $8\frac{1}{2}$ cups of seed. He used $3\frac{3}{4}$ cups, and then used $2\frac{4}{5}$ cups. How many cups of seed are still in the bag?

$$3\frac{3}{4} + 2\frac{4}{5} = 3\frac{15}{20} + 2\frac{16}{20} = 6\frac{11}{20}$$
$$8\frac{1}{2} - 6\frac{11}{20} = 8\frac{10}{20} - 6\frac{11}{20} = 1\frac{19}{20}$$

8. Sarah bought two pieces of material: $\frac{3}{4}$ yd. and $\frac{2}{3}$ yd. long. She used $\frac{7}{8}$ yd. of the material she bought. How much material is left?

$$\frac{3}{4} + \frac{2}{3} = \frac{9}{12} + \frac{8}{12} = 1\frac{5}{12}$$
$$1\frac{5}{12} - \frac{7}{8} = 1\frac{10}{24} = \frac{21}{24} = \frac{13}{24} \textbf{ yd.}$$

9. Ann bought $5\frac{1}{4}$ lb. of vegetables: $1\frac{3}{4}$ lb. of beans, $2\frac{3}{8}$ lb. of carrots, and the rest was cabbage. How many pounds of cabbage did Ann buy?

$$1\frac{3}{4} + 2\frac{3}{8} = 1\frac{6}{8} + 2\frac{3}{8} = 4\frac{1}{8}$$
$$5\frac{1}{4} - 4\frac{1}{8} = 5\frac{2}{8} - 4\frac{1}{8} = 1\frac{1}{8}$$

10. Jim's scout troop went on a trip. They hiked $20\frac{7}{10}$ miles in 3 days. They hiked $7\frac{3}{5}$ miles the first day and $8\frac{3}{4}$ miles the second day. How many miles did they hike the third day?

$$8\frac{3}{4} + 7\frac{3}{5} = 8\frac{15}{20} + 7\frac{12}{20} = 16\frac{7}{20}$$
$$20\frac{7}{10} - 16\frac{7}{20} = 20\frac{14}{20} - 16\frac{7}{20} = 4\frac{7}{20}$$

© Copyright by L. George Saad

WHAT IS THE NUMBER?

Example 1.

What number do you add to $1\frac{1}{2}$ for the answer to be $5\frac{1}{3}$?

Discussion:

Remember that the sum of $1\frac{1}{2}$ and the number is $5\frac{1}{3}$.

The number is $1\frac{1}{2}$ less than $5\frac{1}{3}$.

To find the number, you subtract $1\frac{1}{2}$ from $5\frac{1}{3}$. $5\frac{1}{3} - 1\frac{1}{2} = 5\frac{2}{6} - 1\frac{3}{6} = 3\frac{5}{6}$

Example 2.

What number do you subtract from $9\frac{1}{8}$ for the answer to be $1\frac{3}{4}$?

Discussion:

Remember that the sum of $1\frac{3}{4}$ and the number is $9\frac{1}{8}$.

The number is $1\frac{3}{4}$ less than $9\frac{1}{8}$.

To find the number, you subtract $1\frac{3}{4}$ from $9\frac{1}{8}$. $9\frac{1}{8} - 1\frac{6}{8} = 8\frac{9}{8} - 1\frac{6}{8} = 7\frac{3}{8}$

Example 3.

Study the following equations:

$A = 3\frac{1}{2} + 4\frac{1}{5}$

$B = A - 5\frac{3}{5}$ What number is B?

Discussion:

A is the sum of $3\frac{1}{2}$ and $4\frac{1}{5}$ $A = 3\frac{5}{10} + 4\frac{2}{10} = 7\frac{7}{10}$

To find B, you have to subtract $5\frac{3}{5}$ $B = 7\frac{7}{10} - 5\frac{3}{5} = 7\frac{7}{10} - 5\frac{6}{10} = 2\frac{1}{10}$

from the answer you get for A.

Example 4.

Study the following equation: $N - 7\frac{3}{4} = 2\frac{1}{5}$

What number is N?

Discussion:

The equation is the same as "You subtracted $7\frac{3}{4}$ from a number.

The answer was $2\frac{1}{5}$. What was the number?"

Which of the following processes do you have to carry out?

a. $2\frac{1}{5} + 7\frac{3}{4}$ or   b. $7\frac{3}{4} - 2\frac{1}{5}$ a. $2\frac{1}{5} + 7\frac{3}{4} = 2\frac{4}{20} + 7\frac{15}{20} = 9\frac{19}{20}$

1. What number do you add to $7\frac{1}{2}$ for the sum to be $9\frac{3}{8}$?

$$N = 9\frac{3}{8} - 7\frac{1}{2} = 8\frac{11}{8} - 7\frac{4}{8} = 1\frac{7}{8}$$

2. What number do you subtract from $9\frac{3}{8}$ for the answer to be $7\frac{1}{2}$?

$$N = 9\frac{3}{8} - 7\frac{1}{2}$$
$$= 9\frac{3}{8} - 7\frac{4}{8} = 8\frac{11}{8} - 7\frac{4}{8} = 1\frac{7}{8}$$

3. What number do you subtract from the sum of $9\frac{1}{4}$ and $2\frac{5}{6}$ for the answer to be $5\frac{1}{6}$?

$$9\frac{1}{4} + 2\frac{5}{6} = 9\frac{3}{12} + 2\frac{10}{12} = 12\frac{1}{12}$$
$$12\frac{1}{12} - 5\frac{1}{6} = 12\frac{1}{12} - 5\frac{2}{12} = 6\frac{11}{12}$$

4. $N + 3\frac{1}{4} = 8\frac{1}{3}$
Find the value of N.

$$N = 8\frac{1}{3} - 3\frac{1}{4} = 8\frac{4}{12} - 3\frac{3}{12} = 5\frac{1}{12}$$

5. $17\frac{5}{8} + N = 23\frac{5}{6}$
Find the value of N.

$$N = 23\frac{5}{6} - 17\frac{5}{8} = 23\frac{20}{24} - 17\frac{15}{24} = 6\frac{5}{24}$$

6. $8\frac{3}{4} - B = 1\frac{5}{6}$
Find the value of B.

$$B = 8\frac{3}{4} - 1\frac{5}{6} = 8\frac{9}{12} - 1\frac{10}{12} = 6\frac{11}{12}$$

7. $X - 7\frac{5}{6} = 2\frac{4}{9}$
Find the value of X.

$$X = 2\frac{4}{9} + 7\frac{5}{6} = 2\frac{8}{18} + 7\frac{15}{18} = 10\frac{5}{18}$$

8. $A = 3\frac{1}{4} + 1\frac{7}{8}$
$B = 9 - A$
What number is A?
What number is B?

$$A = 3\frac{2}{8} + 1\frac{7}{8} = 5\frac{1}{8}$$
$$B = 9 - 5\frac{1}{8} = 3\frac{7}{8}$$

B

© Copyright by L. George Saad

Level 15

10 DIVIDING A WHOLE NUMBER BY A FRACTION OR A MIXED NUMBER

Example 1.

Jack mowed 5 acres of grass at the rate of $\frac{3}{4}$ acre per hour.

How many hours did Jack work?

Discussion:

The problem calls for the division: $5 \div \frac{3}{4}$

To find the answer to $5 \div \frac{3}{4}$, you first change 5 into fourths.

$$5 \div \frac{3}{4} = \frac{20}{4} \div \frac{3}{4} = \frac{20}{3} = 6\frac{2}{3}$$

Jack worked for $6\frac{2}{3}$ hours.

Example 2.

Mrs. Jones made 7 quarts of jam.

She has jars, $1\frac{1}{2}$ quarts each.

How many jars will the jam fill?

Discussion:

The problem calls for the division: $7 \div 1\frac{1}{2}$

You first change 7 and $1\frac{1}{2}$ into halves, and then it becomes possible to divide.

$$7 \div 1\frac{1}{2} = \frac{14}{2} \div \frac{3}{2} = \frac{14}{3} = 4\frac{2}{3}$$

4 jars will be completely full, and one jar will be filled to $\frac{2}{3}$ its capacity.

Study the following examples, and then complete the work.

a. $9 \div 1\frac{2}{5} = \frac{45}{5} \div \frac{7}{5} = \frac{45}{7} = \mathbf{6\frac{3}{7}}$

b. $2 \div 4\frac{2}{3} = \frac{6}{3} \div \frac{14}{3} = \frac{6}{14} = \frac{3}{7}$

c. $8 \div 15\frac{1}{4} = \frac{32}{4} \div \frac{61}{4} = \frac{32}{61}$

d. $9 \div 10.8 = 9 \div 10\frac{8}{10} = \frac{90}{10} \div \frac{108}{10} = \frac{90}{108} = \frac{5}{6}$

e. $3 \div 0.14 = 3 \div \frac{14}{100} = \frac{300}{100} \div \frac{14}{100} = \frac{300}{14} = \frac{150}{7} = 21\frac{3}{7}$

f. $2 \div 0.009 = \frac{2000}{1000} \div \frac{9}{1000} = \frac{2000}{9} = 222\frac{2}{9}$

© Copyright by L. George Saad

Divide:

a. $6 \div \frac{2}{3} = \frac{18}{3} \div \frac{2}{3} = \mathbf{9}$

b. $8 \div \frac{4}{5} = \frac{40}{5} \div \frac{4}{5} = \mathbf{10}$

c. $9 \div \frac{3}{8} = \frac{72}{8} \div \frac{3}{8} = \mathbf{24}$

d. $16 \div \frac{2}{5} = \frac{80}{5} \div \frac{2}{5} = \mathbf{40}$

e. $8 \div \frac{3}{4} = \frac{32}{4} \div \frac{3}{4} = \frac{32}{3} = \mathbf{10\frac{2}{3}}$

f. $7 \div \frac{4}{5} = \frac{35}{5} \div \frac{4}{5} = \frac{35}{4} = \mathbf{8\frac{3}{4}}$

g. $3 \div 4\frac{1}{2} = \frac{6}{2} \div \frac{9}{2} = \frac{6}{9} = \mathbf{\frac{2}{3}}$

h. $6 \div 4\frac{1}{2} = \frac{12}{2} \div \frac{9}{2} = \frac{12}{9} = \mathbf{1\frac{1}{3}}$

i. $8 \div 2\frac{2}{5} = \frac{40}{5} \div \frac{12}{5} = \frac{40}{12} = \mathbf{3\frac{1}{3}}$

j. $4 \div 3\frac{4}{7} = \frac{28}{7} \div \frac{25}{7} = \frac{28}{25} = \mathbf{1\frac{3}{25}}$

k. $2 \div 3\frac{1}{2} = \frac{4}{2} \div \frac{7}{2} = \mathbf{\frac{4}{7}}$

l. $5 \div 6\frac{1}{2} = \frac{10}{2} \div \frac{13}{2} = \mathbf{\frac{10}{13}}$

1. AB is 2 inches long and CD is $1\frac{1}{4}$ inches long.
   - AB is how many times as long as CD?
   - CD is how many times as long as AB?

A———————————————B
C——————————D

$2 \div 1\frac{1}{4} = \frac{8}{4} \div \frac{5}{4} = \frac{8}{5} = \mathbf{1\frac{3}{5}}$

$1\frac{1}{4} \div 2 = \frac{5}{4} \div 2 = \frac{5}{4} \div \frac{8}{4} = \mathbf{\frac{5}{8}}$

2. You have a board 12 ft. long. You cut it into pieces, $3\frac{2}{3}$ ft. long each. What is the result?

$12 \div 3\frac{2}{3} = \frac{36}{3} \div \frac{11}{3} = \frac{36}{11} = \mathbf{3\frac{3}{11}}$

3 long pieces and a small piece which is $\frac{3}{11}$ of the long one.

3. Jane lives 4 miles from school. Bob lives $1\frac{1}{5}$ miles from school.
   - Jane lives how many times as far from school as Bob?
   - Bob lives how many times as far from school as Jane?

$4 \div 1\frac{1}{5} = \frac{20}{5} \div \frac{6}{5} = \frac{20}{6} = \mathbf{3\frac{1}{3}}$

$1\frac{1}{5} \div 4 = \frac{6}{5} \div 4 = \frac{6}{20} = \mathbf{\frac{3}{10}}$

4. You multiplied a number by $2\frac{3}{5}$. The answer was 8. What was the number?

$\mathbf{N} = 8 \div 2\frac{3}{5}$
$= \frac{40}{5} \div \frac{13}{5} = \frac{40}{13} = \mathbf{3\frac{1}{13}}$

5. $A = (6 \div 1\frac{1}{4}) - 2.3$ What number is A?

$\mathbf{A} = (\frac{24}{4} \div \frac{5}{4}) - 2.3$
$= 4\frac{4}{5} - 2.3 = 4.8 - 2.3 = \mathbf{2.5}$

© Copyright by L. George Saad

11 DIVIDING BY A FRACTION OF A DIFFERENT UNIT

Example 1.

Your lawn is $\frac{5}{8}$ of an acre.

You can mow $\frac{3}{4}$ of an acre per hour.

How many hours do you need to mow the lawn?

Discussion:

The question may be answered by finding how many $\frac{3}{4}$'s are in $\frac{5}{8}$,

which calls for the division: $\frac{5}{8} \div \frac{3}{4}$.

• How can you do this division?

You need to have the two fractions in the same fractional unit.

• You need to change $\frac{3}{4}$ into $\frac{6}{8}$, then the division becomes $\frac{5}{8} \div \frac{6}{8}$.

$$\frac{5}{8} \div \frac{3}{4} = \frac{5}{8} \div \frac{6}{8} = \frac{5}{6}$$

You need $\frac{5}{6}$ of an hour to mow the $\frac{5}{8}$ of an acre.

Example 2.

Bill put $\frac{7}{10}$ gallon of milk in a $\frac{3}{4}$ gallon container.

How much of the container is filled with milk?

Discussion:

• The question may be answered by finding how many $\frac{3}{4}$'s are in $\frac{7}{10}$,

which calls for the division $\frac{7}{10} \div \frac{3}{4}$.

• To do the division you need to have the two fractions in the same fractional unit.

• We may change $\frac{7}{10}$ into $\frac{14}{20}$ and $\frac{3}{4}$ into $\frac{15}{20}$, then the division becomes $\frac{14}{20} \div \frac{15}{20} = \frac{14}{15}$.

$\frac{14}{15}$ of the container is filled with milk.

Example 3.

Usually Ted spends $\frac{2}{5}$ of an hour exercising.

Today he spent $\frac{3}{4}$ of an hour.

How much did he practice today compared to his regular time?

Discussion:

• The question may be answered by finding how many $\frac{2}{5}$'s are in $\frac{3}{4}$,

which calls for the division $\frac{3}{4} \div \frac{2}{5}$.

• To do the division you need to have the two fractions in the same fractional unit.

$$\frac{3}{4} \div \frac{2}{5} = \frac{15}{20} \div \frac{8}{20} = \frac{15}{8} = 1\frac{7}{8}$$

Ted exercised $1\frac{7}{8}$ times as long as he used to exercise.

34

© Copyright by L. George Saad

Divide:

a. $\frac{1}{3} \div \frac{1}{6} = \frac{2}{6} \div \frac{1}{6} = \frac{2}{1} = 2$

b. $\frac{1}{4} \div \frac{5}{8} = \frac{2}{8} \div \frac{5}{8} = \frac{2}{5}$

c. $\frac{7}{9} \div \frac{1}{3} = \frac{7}{9} \div \frac{3}{9} = \frac{7}{3} = 2\frac{1}{3}$

d. $\frac{7}{12} \div \frac{3}{4} = \frac{7}{12} \div \frac{9}{12} = \frac{7}{9}$

e. $\frac{5}{6} \div \frac{2}{9} = \frac{15}{18} \div \frac{4}{18} = \frac{15}{4} = 3\frac{3}{4}$

f. $\frac{9}{10} \div \frac{3}{4} = \frac{18}{20} \div \frac{15}{20} = \frac{18}{15} = \frac{6}{5} = 1\frac{1}{5}$

g. $\frac{7}{8} \div \frac{5}{6} = \frac{21}{24} \div \frac{20}{24} = \frac{21}{20} = 1\frac{1}{20}$

h. $\frac{3}{4} \div \frac{1}{6} = \frac{9}{12} \div \frac{2}{12} = \frac{9}{2} = 4\frac{1}{2}$

i. $\frac{3}{10} \div \frac{7}{15} = \frac{9}{30} \div \frac{14}{30} = \frac{9}{14}$

j. $\frac{3}{8} \div \frac{7}{12} = \frac{9}{24} \div \frac{14}{24} = \frac{9}{14}$

k. $0.5 \div \frac{2}{5} = \frac{5}{10} \div \frac{4}{10} = \frac{5}{4} = 1\frac{1}{4}$

l. $\frac{2}{3} \div 0.7 = \frac{2}{3} \div \frac{7}{10} = \frac{20}{30} \div \frac{21}{30} = \frac{20}{21}$

m. $0.12 \div \frac{1}{2} = \frac{12}{100} \div \frac{50}{100} = \frac{12}{50} = \frac{6}{25}$

n. $0.21 \div 0.4 = \frac{21}{100} \div \frac{40}{100} = \frac{21}{40}$

1. Sue completes a job in $\frac{5}{6}$ of an hour. What part of the job would she finish in $\frac{1}{4}$ of an hour?

   $\frac{1}{4} \div \frac{5}{6} = \frac{3}{12} \div \frac{10}{12} = \frac{3}{10}$
   $\frac{3}{10}$ of the job would be finished.

2. You poured $\frac{1}{2}$ a gallon of milk in a container which holds $\frac{3}{4}$ gallon. What was the result?

   $\frac{1}{2} \div \frac{3}{4} = \frac{2}{4} \div \frac{3}{4} = \frac{2}{3}$
   $\frac{2}{3}$ of the container is filled.

3. Jim ran $\frac{4}{5}$ of a mile, at a speed of $\frac{2}{25}$ of a mile per minute. How many minutes did he run?

   $\frac{4}{5} \div \frac{2}{25} = \frac{20}{25} \div \frac{2}{25} = \frac{20}{2} = 10$
   He ran 10 minutes.

4. Bob cut $\frac{7}{8}$ lb. of meat equally into pieces $\frac{1}{4}$ lb. each. What was the result?

   $\frac{7}{8} \div \frac{1}{4} = \frac{7}{8} \div \frac{2}{8} = \frac{7}{2} = 3\frac{1}{2}$
   3 big pieces and a small piece which weighs half the big one.

5. A rod is $\frac{7}{8}$ yd. long. You cut a piece $\frac{3}{4}$ yd. long. What fraction of the rod did you cut?

   $\frac{3}{4} \div \frac{7}{8} = \frac{6}{8} \div \frac{7}{8} = \frac{6}{7}$
   $\frac{6}{7}$ of the rod was cut.

B

© Copyright by L. George Saad

Level 15

12 DIVIDING BY A FRACTION OR A MIXED NUMBER

Example 1.

You had a rope $6\frac{2}{3}$ yards long.

You cut the rope into pieces $\frac{3}{4}$ yd. long each.

What was the result?

Discussion:

The question is the same as "How many $\frac{3}{4}$'s are in $6\frac{2}{3}$?",

which calls for the division: $6\frac{2}{3} \div \frac{3}{4}$.

You first change $6\frac{2}{3}$ into thirds. The division becomes $\frac{20}{3} \div \frac{3}{4}$, which you can do.

$$6\frac{2}{3} \div \frac{3}{4} = \frac{20}{3} \div \frac{3}{4} = \frac{80}{12} \div \frac{9}{12} = \frac{80}{9} = 8\frac{8}{9}$$

The result was 8 long pieces and a short one whose length is 8 ninths that of the long piece.

B

Example 2.

AB is $2\frac{1}{8}$ inches.

XY is $1\frac{3}{4}$ inches.

AB is how many times as long as XY?

A ————————————— B
X ————————————— Y

Discussion:

The question is the same as "How many $1\frac{3}{4}$'s are in $2\frac{1}{8}$?"

which calls for the division: $2\frac{1}{8} \div 1\frac{3}{4}$ which is the same as $\frac{17}{8} \div \frac{7}{4}$.

To do this division you first have to change the two fractions into the same fractional unit as shown below.

$$\frac{17}{8} \div \frac{14}{8} = \frac{17}{8} \div \frac{8}{14} = \frac{17}{14} = 1\frac{3}{14}$$

AB is $1\frac{3}{14}$ times as long as XY.

Example 3.

How many $3\frac{3}{8}$'s are in $1\frac{5}{6}$?

Discussion:

The question calls for the division: $1\frac{5}{6} \div 3\frac{3}{8}$

$$1\frac{5}{6} \div 3\frac{3}{8} = \frac{11}{6} \div \frac{27}{8} = \frac{44}{24} \div \frac{81}{24} = \frac{44}{81}$$ $1\frac{5}{6}$ is $\frac{44}{81}$ times $3\frac{3}{8}$.

Example 4.

Divide 3.5 by $1\frac{3}{8}$.

Solution:

$$3.5 \div 1\frac{3}{8} = \frac{35}{10} \div \frac{11}{8} = \frac{140}{40} \div \frac{55}{40} = \frac{140}{55} = 2\frac{30}{55} = 2\frac{6}{11}$$

Level 15

© Copyright by L. George Saad

Divide:

a. $8\frac{1}{2} \div 1\frac{1}{4} = \frac{17}{2} \div \frac{5}{4} = \frac{34}{4} \div \frac{5}{4} = \frac{34}{5} = 6\frac{4}{5}$

b. $2\frac{7}{10} \div 1\frac{4}{5} = \frac{27}{10} \div \frac{9}{5} = \frac{27}{10} \div \frac{18}{10} = \frac{27}{18} = 1\frac{1}{2}$

c. $3\frac{1}{2} \div 1\frac{1}{3} = \frac{7}{2} \div \frac{4}{3} = \frac{21}{6} \div \frac{8}{6} = \frac{21}{8} = 2\frac{5}{8}$

d. $2\frac{1}{3} \div 4\frac{1}{4} = \frac{7}{3} \div \frac{17}{4} = \frac{28}{12} \div \frac{51}{12} = \frac{28}{51}$

e. $3\frac{5}{8} \div 4\frac{1}{6} = \frac{29}{8} \div \frac{25}{6} = \frac{87}{24} \div \frac{100}{24} = \frac{87}{100}$

f. $5\frac{2}{5} \div 1.2 = \frac{27}{5} \div \frac{12}{10} = \frac{54}{10} \div \frac{12}{10} = \frac{54}{12} = 4\frac{1}{2}$

g. $3.7 \div 2\frac{1}{2} = \frac{37}{10} \div \frac{5}{2} = \frac{37}{10} \div \frac{25}{10} = \frac{37}{25} = 1\frac{12}{25}$

h. $7.5 \div 1.25 = \frac{75}{10} \div \frac{125}{100} = \frac{750}{100} \div \frac{125}{100} = \frac{750}{125} = 6$

1. You covered $3\frac{3}{10}$ miles on your bicycle at a speed of $2\frac{3}{4}$ miles per hour. How much time did you ride your bicycle?

   $3\frac{3}{10} \div 2\frac{3}{4} = \frac{33}{10} \div \frac{11}{4}$
   $= \frac{66}{20} \div \frac{55}{20} = \frac{66}{55} = 1\frac{1}{5}$ hrs.

2. A farmer had $10\frac{5}{8}$ bushels of corn. He put the corn in containers which held $2\frac{1}{2}$ bushels each. How many containers did the corn fill?

   $10\frac{5}{8} \div 2\frac{1}{2} = \frac{85}{8} \div \frac{5}{2}$
   $= \frac{85}{8} \div \frac{20}{8} = \frac{85}{20} = 4\frac{1}{4}$

3. One yard is approximately $\frac{32}{35}$ of a meter. How many yards are in $7\frac{1}{5}$ meters?

   $7\frac{1}{5} \div \frac{32}{35} = \frac{36}{5} \div \frac{32}{35}$
   $= \frac{252}{35} \div \frac{32}{35} = \frac{252}{32} = 7\frac{7}{8}$

4. One meter is approximately $1\frac{3}{32}$ yds. How many meters are in $9\frac{5}{8}$ yds?

   $9\frac{5}{8} \div 1\frac{3}{32} = \frac{77}{8} \div \frac{35}{32}$
   $= \frac{308}{32} \div \frac{35}{32} = \frac{308}{35} = 8\frac{4}{5}$

5. One kilogram is approximately equivalent to $2\frac{1}{5}$ pounds. How many kilograms are in $5\frac{1}{2}$ pounds?

   $5\frac{1}{2} \div 2\frac{1}{5} = \frac{11}{2} \div \frac{11}{5}$
   $= \frac{55}{10} \div \frac{22}{10} = \frac{55}{22} = 2\frac{1}{2}$

B

© Copyright by L. George Saad

Level 15

13 DIVIDING BY A DECIMAL

You know how to divide a decimal by a whole number. Do the following exercises:

1.	2.	3.
$\quad\underline{047.9}$ 5) 239.5	$\quad\underline{12.09}$ 7) 84.63	$\quad\underline{1.158}$ 8) 9.264

4.	5.	6.
$\quad\underline{005.9}$ 25) 147.5 $\quad\underline{125}$ $\quad225$ $\quad\underline{225}$	$\quad\underline{01.79}$ 24) 42.96 $\quad\underline{24}$ $\quad189$ $\quad\underline{168}$ $\quad216$ $\quad\underline{216}$	$\quad\underline{0.176}$ 48) 8.448 $\quad\underline{48}$ $\quad364$ $\quad\underline{336}$ $\quad288$ $\quad\underline{288}$

7.	8.	9.
$\quad\underline{01.68}$ 25) 42.00 $\quad\underline{25}$ $\quad170$ $\quad\underline{150}$ $\quad200$ $\quad\underline{200}$	$\quad\underline{0.124}$ 75) 9.300 $\quad\underline{75}$ $\quad180$ $\quad\underline{150}$ $\quad300$ $\quad\underline{300}$	$\quad\underline{00.125}$ 224) 28.000 $\quad\underline{22\ 4}$ $\quad5\ 60$ $\quad\underline{4\ 48}$ $\quad1\ 120$ $\quad\underline{1\ 120}$

Example 1:

Divide: $78 \div 0.3$

Solution:

$78 \div 0.3 = 78 \div \frac{3}{10}$

$\quad = \frac{780}{10} \div \frac{31}{10}$

$\quad = 780 \div 3 = 260$

$$\begin{array}{r} 260 \\ 3)\overline{780} \end{array}$$

Example 2:

Divide: $153 \div 0.09$

Solution:

$153 \div 0.09 = 153 \div \frac{9}{100}$

$\quad = \frac{15300}{100} \quad \frac{.9}{100} \quad =$

$\quad = 15300 \div 9 = 1700$

$$\begin{array}{r} 01700 \\ 9)\overline{15300} \end{array}$$

Example 3:

Divide: $372 \div 1.6$

Solution:

$372 \div 1.6 = 372 \div \frac{16}{10}$

$\quad = \frac{3720}{100} \quad \frac{.16}{10}$

$\quad = 3720 \div 16$

$\quad = 232.5$

$$\begin{array}{r} 0232.5 \\ 16)\overline{3720.0} \\ \underline{32} \\ 52 \\ \underline{48} \\ 40 \\ \underline{32} \\ 80 \\ \underline{80} \end{array}$$

Example 4:

Divide: $52 \div 2.08$

Solution:

$52 \div 2.08 = 52 \div \frac{208}{100}$

$\quad = \frac{5200}{100} \quad \frac{208}{100}$

$\quad = 5200 \div 208$

$\quad = 25$

$$\begin{array}{r} 0025 \\ 208)\overline{5200} \\ \underline{416} \\ 1040 \\ \underline{1040} \end{array}$$

© Copyright by L. George Saad

EXERCISE

Divide:

a. $75 \div 1.5$
$75 \div \frac{15}{10}$
$\frac{750}{10} \div \frac{15}{10}$
$750 \div 15 = 50$

b. $36 \div 1.44$
$36 \div \frac{144}{100}$
$\frac{3600}{100} \div \frac{144}{100}$
$3600 \div 144 = 25$

c. $35 \div 0.14$
$35 \div \frac{14}{100}$
$\frac{3500}{100} \div \frac{14}{100}$
$3500 \div 14 = 250$

d. $574 \div 16.4$
$\frac{5740}{10} \div \frac{164}{10}$
$5740 \div 164 = 35$

e. $715 \div 2.75$
$\frac{71500}{100} \div \frac{275}{100}$
$71500 \div 275 = 260$

f. $8 \div 0.125$
$\frac{8000}{1000} \div \frac{125}{1000}$
$8000 \div 125 = 64$

g. $30 \div 2.4$
$\frac{300}{10} \div \frac{24}{10}$
$300 \div 24 = 12.5$

h. $72 \div 0.45$
$\frac{7200}{100} \div \frac{45}{100}$
$7200 \div 45 = 160$

i. $93 \div 0.15$
$\frac{9300}{100} \div \frac{15}{100}$
$9300 \div 15 = 620$

APPLICATIONS

1. The product of two numbers is 39. One number is 5.2. What is the other number?

```
        007.5
52) 390.0
    364
    260
    260
```

The other number is __7.5__

2. In a division exercise, the dividend is 230, and the quotient is 18.4. Find the divisor.

```
         0012.5
184) 2300.0
     184
     460
     368
     920
     920
```

The divisor is __12.5__

3. In a division exercise, the divisor was 1.25 and the dividend was 8. Find the quotient.

```
        006.4
125) 800.0
     750
     500
     500
```

The quotient is __6.4__

4. $5.6 \times N = 35$
What number is N?

```
         006.25
56) 350.00
    336
    140
    112
    280
    280
```

N is __6.25__

© Copyright by L. George Saad

Level 15

Example 5.

Mary bought fabric for $1.25 per yard.

She paid $6.75.

How many yards of fabric did she buy?

$$
\begin{array}{r}
005.4 \\
125\overline{)\,675.0} \\
625 \\
\hline
500 \\
500 \\
\hline
\end{array}
$$

Discussion:

The problem calls for the division: $6.75 \div 1.25$

$$6.75 \div 1.25 = \frac{675}{100} \div \frac{125}{100} = 675 \div 125$$

We divided 675 by 125 as shown to the right.   The answer is 5.4

Mary bought 5.4 yards of fabric.

Example 6.

Divide: $5.74 \div 0.7$

$$
\begin{array}{r}
008.2 \\
70\overline{)\,574.0} \\
560 \\
\hline
140 \\
140 \\
\hline
\end{array}
$$

Solution:

$$5.74 \div 0.7 = \frac{574}{100} \div \frac{7}{10}$$
$$= \frac{574}{100} \div \frac{70}{100}$$
$$= 574 \div 70 = 8.2$$

Another way:

You also may change both dividend and divisor into tenths:

$$5.74 \div 0.7 = \frac{57.4}{10} \div \frac{7}{10} = 57.4 \div 7$$

$$
\begin{array}{r}
08.2 \\
7\overline{)\,57.4}
\end{array}
$$

Example 7.

Divide: $8.528 \div 3.28$

$$
\begin{array}{r}
002.6 \\
328\overline{)\,852.8} \\
656 \\
\hline
1968 \\
1968 \\
\hline
\end{array}
$$

Discussion:

Dividing 8.528 by 3.28 is the same
as dividing 852.8 by 328.

Why?

$$8.528 \div 3.28 = \frac{852.8}{100} \div \frac{328}{100} = 352.8 \div 328$$

Complete the work.

© Copyright by L. George Saad

Divide.

1. 72.8 by 2.8 $\frac{728}{10} \div \frac{28}{10}$ $728 \div 28 = 26$	2. 78.75 by 2.25 $\frac{7875}{100} \div \frac{225}{100}$ $7875 \div 225 = 35$	3. 1.652 ÷ .059 $\frac{1652}{1000} \div \frac{59}{1000}$ $1652 \div 59 = 28$
4. 17.55 ÷ 4.5 $\frac{175.5}{10} \div \frac{45}{10}$ $175.5 \div 45 = 3.9$	5. 20.88 ÷ 3.6 $\frac{208.8}{10} \div \frac{36}{10}$ $208.8 \div 36 = 5.8$	6. 2.205 ÷ 0.63 $\frac{220.5}{100} \div \frac{63}{100}$ $220.5 \div 63 = 3.5$
7. 374.1 ÷ 1.29 $\frac{37410}{100} \div \frac{129}{100}$ $37410 \div 129 = 290$	8. 25.35 ÷ 6.5 $\frac{253.5}{10} \div \frac{65}{10}$ $253.5 \div 65 = 3.9$	9. 140.5 ÷ 5.62 $\frac{14050}{100} \div \frac{562}{100}$ $14050 \div 562 = 25$

APPLICATIONS

1. You multiplied a number by 0.43. The answer was 12.47. What was the number?

```
       0029
43) 1247
     86
    387
    387
```

The number is __29__

2. Divide the sum of 3.06 and 5.2 by the difference between 6.15 and 3.2

```
        002.8
295) 826.0
      590
     2360
     2360
```

The answer is __2.8__

3. In a division exercise, the divisor is 1.25, and the dividend is 0.8. Find the quotient.

```
        00.64
125) 80.00
      75 0
       5 00
       5 00
```

The quotient is __0.64__

4. N x 12.6 = 0.756. What number is N?

```
          000.06
12600) 756.00
        756.00
```

N is __0.06__

© Copyright by L. George Saad

UNIT B TEST

1. To add $\frac{1}{2}$ and $\frac{1}{3}$, we have to change $\frac{1}{2}$ into $\frac{3}{6}$ and $\frac{1}{3}$ into $\frac{2}{6}$.
   Why do we do so? <u>**To add fractions, they have to be in the same unit**</u>

2. Add:

   a. $\frac{1}{2} + \frac{1}{4} = \frac{2}{4} + \frac{1}{4} = \frac{3}{4}$

   e. $\begin{aligned} 7\frac{5}{6} &= 7\frac{20}{24} \\ + 3\frac{7}{8} &= 3\frac{21}{24} \\ \hline 10\frac{41}{24} &= 11\frac{17}{24} \end{aligned}$

   b. $\frac{3}{4} + \frac{4}{5} = \frac{15}{20} + \frac{16}{20} = \frac{31}{20} = 1\frac{11}{20}$

   c. $1\frac{2}{5} + 5\frac{2}{3} = 1\frac{6}{15} + 5\frac{10}{15} = 6\frac{16}{15} = 7\frac{1}{15}$

   f. $\begin{aligned} 9\frac{1}{5} &= 9\frac{8}{40} \\ + 5\frac{7}{8} &= 5\frac{35}{40} \\ \hline 14\frac{43}{40} &= 15\frac{3}{40} \end{aligned}$

   d. $3\frac{5}{6} + 2\frac{3}{8} = 3\frac{20}{24} + 2\frac{9}{24} = 5\frac{29}{24} = 6\frac{5}{24}$

3. Subtract:

   a. $\frac{1}{3} - \frac{1}{5} = \frac{5}{15} - \frac{3}{15} = \frac{2}{15}$

   e. $\begin{aligned} 9\frac{1}{4} &= 9\frac{2}{8} = 8\frac{10}{8} \\ - 1\frac{5}{8} &= 1\frac{5}{8} = 1\frac{5}{8} \\ \hline & \qquad\qquad 7\frac{5}{8} \end{aligned}$

   b. $\frac{7}{8} - \frac{5}{6} = \frac{21}{24} - \frac{20}{24} = \frac{1}{24}$

   c. $8\frac{1}{4} - 1\frac{5}{6} = 8\frac{3}{12} - 1\frac{10}{12} = 6\frac{5}{12}$

   f. $\begin{aligned} 7\frac{4}{9} &= 7\frac{8}{18} = 6\frac{26}{18} \\ - 5\frac{5}{6} &= 5\frac{15}{18} = 5\frac{15}{18} \\ \hline & \qquad\qquad 1\frac{11}{18} \end{aligned}$

   d. $7\frac{5}{6} - 1\frac{7}{9} = 7\frac{15}{18} - 1\frac{14}{18} = 6\frac{1}{18}$

4. Sue spent $1\frac{1}{4}$ hr. working on mathematics, $1\frac{1}{2}$ hr. on English, and $\frac{4}{5}$ hr. on science. How much time did she spend studying?

   $1\frac{5}{20} + 1\frac{10}{20} + \frac{16}{20} = 2\frac{31}{20} = 3\frac{11}{20}$ hr.

5. The sum of two numbers is $7\frac{1}{3}$. One of the numbers is $3\frac{3}{5}$. What is the other number?

   $7\frac{1}{3} - 3\frac{3}{5} = 7\frac{5}{15} - 3\frac{9}{15} = 3\frac{11}{15}$

6. Jill bought two pieces of material: $2\frac{1}{2}$ yd. and $3\frac{1}{3}$ yd. long. She made a dress and she had $1\frac{3}{4}$ yd. left. How many yards of material did she use?

   $2\frac{1}{2} + 3\frac{1}{3} = 2\frac{3}{6} + 3\frac{2}{6} = 5\frac{5}{6}$
   $5\frac{5}{6} - 1\frac{3}{4} = 5\frac{10}{12} - 1\frac{9}{12} = 4\frac{1}{12}$

© Copyright by L. George Saad

7. Divide:

a. $\frac{1}{2} \div \frac{3}{8} = \frac{4}{8} \div \frac{3}{8} = \frac{4}{3} = 1\frac{1}{3}$

b. $\frac{4}{5} \div \frac{1}{3} = \frac{12}{15} \div \frac{5}{15} = \frac{12}{5} = 2\frac{2}{5}$

c. $\frac{3}{4} \div \frac{5}{6} = \frac{9}{12} \div \frac{10}{12} = \frac{9}{10}$

d. $\frac{5}{8} \div \frac{5}{12} = \frac{15}{24} \div \frac{10}{24} = \frac{15}{10} = 1\frac{1}{2}$

8. Divide;

a. $8 \div \frac{2}{5} = \frac{40}{5} \div \frac{2}{5} = \frac{40}{2} = 20$

b. $5 \div \frac{3}{4} = \frac{20}{4} \div \frac{3}{4} = \frac{20}{3} = 6\frac{2}{3}$

c. $9 \div 1\frac{1}{2} = \frac{18}{2} \div \frac{3}{2} = \frac{18}{3} = 6$

d. $10 \div 1\frac{3}{4} = \frac{40}{4} \div \frac{7}{4} = \frac{40}{7} = 5\frac{5}{7}$

9. Divide:

a. $9\frac{1}{3} \div \frac{5}{9} = \frac{28}{3} \div \frac{5}{9} = \frac{84}{9} \div \frac{5}{9} = \frac{84}{5} = 16\frac{4}{5}$

b. $3\frac{3}{4} \div 1\frac{2}{3} = \frac{15}{4} \div \frac{5}{3} = \frac{45}{12} \div \frac{20}{12} = \frac{45}{20} = 2\frac{1}{4}$

c. $5\frac{3}{5} \div 2\frac{1}{2} = \frac{28}{5} \div \frac{5}{2} = \frac{56}{10} \div \frac{25}{10} = \frac{56}{25} = 2\frac{6}{25}$

10. Divide:

a. $15 \div 0.3$
$= \frac{150}{10} \div \frac{3}{10} = 50$

b. $140.4 \div 3.6$
$= \frac{1404}{10} \div \frac{36}{10}$
$= 1404 \div 36 = 39$

c. $4.41 \div 12.6$
$= \frac{441}{100} \div \frac{1260}{100}$
$= 441 \div 1260 = 0.35$

11. John needs 10 hours to complete a project.
He works for $1\frac{2}{3}$ hours each day.
In how many days does he complete this project? $10 \div 1\frac{2}{3} = \frac{30}{3} \div \frac{5}{3} = \frac{30}{5} = 6$

12. One week Jane babysat for 9 hours.
She made $15.75.
How much does she make per hour? $\$15.75 \div 9 = \$1.75$

13. You put $5\frac{3}{4}$ lb. of jam in jars which
held $1\frac{1}{2}$ lb. each. $5\frac{3}{4} \div 1\frac{1}{2} = \frac{23}{4} \div \frac{3}{2} = \frac{23}{4} \div \frac{6}{4} = \frac{23}{6} = 3\frac{5}{6}$
What was the result?   **3 jars are filled, and one is 5-sixth filled.**

14. Find the answer:

a. $(3\frac{1}{4} + \frac{1}{2}) \div \frac{3}{8}$ $3\frac{3}{4} \div \frac{3}{8} = \frac{15}{4} \div \frac{3}{8} = \frac{30}{8} \div \frac{3}{8} = 10$

b. $(8 \div 1\frac{2}{5}) + \frac{2}{7}$ $(\frac{40}{5} \div \frac{7}{5}) + \frac{2}{7} = \frac{40}{7} + \frac{2}{7} = \frac{42}{7} = 6$

© Copyright by L. George Saad   **Level 15**

14   A FRACTION OF ONE TIME

Example 1.

The three figures in each set are the same size.

- In picture A, there are 2 sets with
3 wholes in each set.
The picture represents 3 taken twice.
2 x 3 is shaded.

- In picture B, there is 1 set with
3 wholes in the set.
The picture represents 3 taken one time.
1 x 3 is shaded.

- In picture C, there is 1 set of 3 wholes,
and the set is cut into 2 equal parts.
You may say that the picture represents 3
taken one-half of one time.
$\frac{1}{2}$ x 3 is shaded.

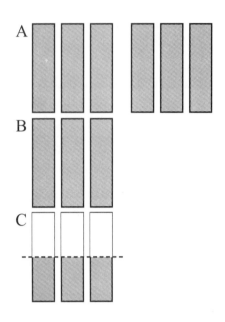

Example 2.

The four figures are the same size. The set is cut into 3 equal parts.

a. The shaded area represents 4
taken one-third of one time.

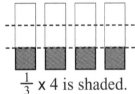

$\frac{1}{3}$ x 4 is shaded.

b. The shaded area represents 4
taken two-thirds of one time.

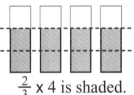

$\frac{2}{3}$ x 4 is shaded.

Example 3.

The five figures are the same size. The set is cut into 6 equal parts.

a. The shaded area represents 5
taken one-sixth of one time.

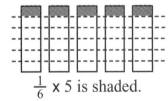

$\frac{1}{6}$ x 5 is shaded.

b. The shaded area represents 5
taken five-sixths of one time.

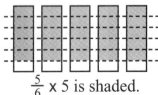

$\frac{5}{6}$ x 5 is shaded.

© Copyright by L. George Saad

APPLICATIONS

In each question, the figures are the same size, and the set of figures is cut into equal parts. Write the multiplication represented by the picture.

a.

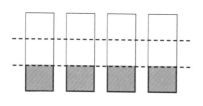

$\frac{1}{3} \times 4$

b.

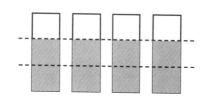

$\frac{2}{3} \times 4$

c.

$\frac{1}{4} \times 3$

d.

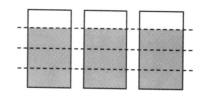

$\frac{3}{4} \times 3$

e.

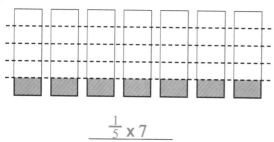

$\frac{1}{5} \times 7$

f.

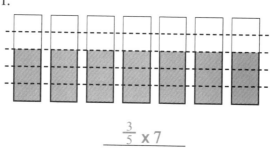

$\frac{3}{5} \times 7$

g.

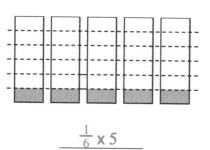

$\frac{1}{6} \times 5$

h.

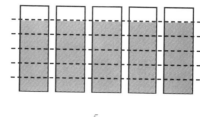

$\frac{5}{6} \times 5$

© Copyright by L. George Saad

45

15 A FRACTIONAL UNIT X A WHOLE NUMBER

Example 1.

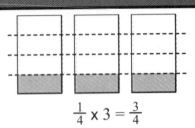

The figures are the same size.

$\frac{1}{4}$ x 3 is shaded.

1-fourth of each of the 3 figures is shaded.

3 fourths are shaded.

The shaded area is equivalent to 3 fourths of one figure.

$$\frac{1}{4} \times 3 = \frac{3}{4}$$

Example 2.

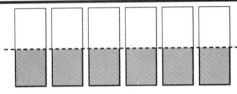

The figures are the same size.

$\frac{1}{2}$ x 6 is shaded.

1-half of each of the 6 figures is shaded.

6 halves are shaded.

The shaded area is equivalent to that of 3 figures.

$$\frac{1}{2} \times 6 = \frac{6}{2} = 3$$

Example 3.

The figures are the same size.

• What does the shaded area represent?

   $\frac{1}{3}$ x 5

• Write the multiplication equation.

   $\frac{1}{3}$ x 5 = $\frac{5}{3}$ = $1\frac{2}{3}$

• What does the answer mean?

   The shaded area is equivalent to that of $1\frac{2}{3}$ figures.

Example 4.

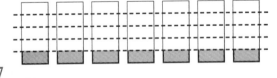

The figures are the same size.

• What does the shaded area represent?

   $\frac{1}{5}$ x 7

• Write the multiplication equation.

   $\frac{1}{5}$ x 7 = $\frac{7}{5}$ = $1\frac{2}{5}$

• What does the answer mean?

   The shaded area is equivalent to that of $1\frac{2}{5}$ figures.

Study the following examples.

a. $\frac{1}{4}$ x 12 = $\frac{12}{4}$ = 3

b. $\frac{1}{8}$ x 19 = $\frac{19}{8}$ = $2\frac{3}{8}$

c. $\frac{1}{6}$ x 22 = $\frac{22}{6}$ = $3\frac{4}{6}$ = $3\frac{2}{3}$

© Copyright by L. George Saad

Multiply:

a. $\frac{1}{3} \times 2 = \frac{2}{3}$ b. $\frac{1}{6} \times 5 = \frac{5}{6}$

c. $\frac{1}{8} \times 7 = \frac{7}{8}$ d. $\frac{1}{9} \times 4 = \frac{4}{9}$

e. $\frac{1}{2} \times 8 = \frac{8}{2} = 4$ f. $\frac{1}{3} \times 18 = \frac{18}{3} = 6$

g. $\frac{1}{7} \times 14 = \frac{14}{7} = 2$ h. $\frac{1}{6} \times 30 = \frac{30}{6} = 5$

i. $\frac{1}{2} \times 3 = \frac{3}{2} = 1\frac{1}{2}$ j. $\frac{1}{3} \times 5 = \frac{5}{3} = 1\frac{2}{3}$

k. $\frac{1}{4} \times 9 = \frac{9}{4} = 2\frac{1}{4}$ l. $\frac{1}{5} \times 12 = \frac{12}{5} = 2\frac{2}{5}$

m. $\frac{1}{4} \times 22 = \frac{22}{4} = 5\frac{2}{4} = 5\frac{1}{2}$ n. $\frac{1}{6} \times 20 = \frac{20}{6} = 3\frac{2}{6} = 3\frac{1}{3}$

APPLICATIONS

Write multiplication equations:

1. You filled a 5-gallon container to $\frac{1}{3}$ of its capacity with milk.
   How many gallons of milk did you use?

   $\frac{1}{3} \times 5 = \frac{5}{3} = 1\frac{2}{3}$

2. A dairy farmer had 30 lbs. of cheese.
   After some time, the cheese lost $\frac{1}{8}$ of its weight.
   How many pounds did the weight decrease?

   $\frac{1}{8} \times 30 = \frac{30}{8} = 3\frac{6}{8} = 3\frac{3}{4}$

3. You have covered $\frac{1}{6}$ of the 20 miles between two villages.
   How many miles did you cover?

   $\frac{1}{6} \times 20 = \frac{20}{6} = \frac{10}{3} = 3\frac{1}{3}$

4. A man is 42 years old.
   His son's age is $\frac{1}{5}$ of his own.
   How old is the son?

   $\frac{1}{5} \times 42 = \frac{42}{5} = 8\frac{2}{5}$

5. Find the answer:
   a. $9 - (\frac{1}{3} \times 8)$
   b. $(\frac{1}{4} \times 3) + (\frac{1}{8} \times 5)$

   a. $9 - \frac{8}{3} = 9 - 2\frac{2}{3} = 6\frac{1}{3}$
   b. $\frac{3}{4} + \frac{5}{8} + \frac{6}{8} = \frac{5}{8} = 1\frac{3}{8}$

© Copyright by L. George Saad   **Level 15**

16   A FRACTION X A WHOLE NUMBER

Example 1.

The figures are the same size.

$\frac{2}{3}$ x 4 is shaded.

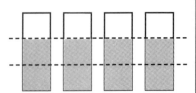

- The colored area is made of 2 rows of thirds, with 4 thirds in each row.
- The colored area is made of (2 x 4) thirds.
- The colored area is 8 thirds.

The colored area is $2\frac{2}{3}$ times as much as one figure.

$$\frac{2}{3} \times 4 = \frac{2 \times 4}{3} = \frac{8}{3} = 2\frac{2}{3}$$

Example 2.

The figures are the same size.

$\frac{3}{4}$ x 5 is shaded.

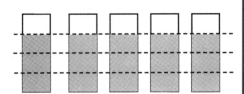

- The colored area is made of 3 rows of fourths, with 5 fourths in each row.
- The colored area is made of (3 x 5) fourths.
- The colored area is 15 fourths.

The colored area is $3\frac{3}{4}$ times as much as one figure.

$$\frac{3}{4} \times 5 = \frac{3 \times 5}{4} = \frac{15}{4} = 3\frac{3}{4}$$

Example 3.

Find the value of $\frac{6}{7}$ x 3.

Discussion:

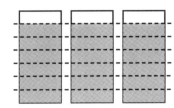

- The colored area is made of sevenths.

    How many rows?   6

    How many $\frac{1}{7}$'s are in each row?   3

    In all, how many sevenths?   18

$$\frac{6}{7} \times 3 = \frac{6 \times 3}{7} = \frac{18}{7} = 2\frac{4}{7}$$

Example 4.

Show that $\frac{2}{5}$ x 7 is the same as 14 fifths.

Solution:

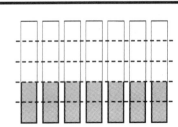

The figures are the same size.

$\frac{2}{5}$ x 7 fifths is shaded.

- The shaded area is made of 2 rows of fifths, with 7 fifths in each row.
- The shaded area is made of (2 x 7) fifths.
- The shaded area is 14 fifths.

Level 15   © Copyright by L. George Saad

Multiply:

a. $\frac{2}{7} \times 3 = \frac{6}{7}$

b. $\frac{4}{9} \times 2 = \frac{8}{9}$

c. $\frac{2}{5} \times 8 = \frac{16}{5} = 3\frac{1}{5}$

d. $\frac{3}{8} \times 9 = \frac{27}{8} = 3\frac{3}{8}$

e. $\frac{6}{7} \times 10 = \frac{60}{7} = 8\frac{4}{7}$

f. $\frac{3}{4} \times 11 = \frac{33}{4} = 8\frac{1}{4}$

g. $\frac{7}{10} \times 9 = \frac{63}{10} = 6\frac{3}{10}$

h. $\frac{2}{3} \times 13 = \frac{26}{3} = 8\frac{2}{3}$

i. $\frac{3}{8} \times 13 = \frac{39}{8} = 4\frac{7}{8}$

j. $\frac{7}{8} \times 9 = \frac{63}{8} = 7\frac{7}{8}$

k. $\frac{9}{10} \times 19 = \frac{171}{10} = 17\frac{1}{10}$

l. $\frac{2}{7} \times 50 = \frac{100}{7} = 14\frac{2}{7}$

m. $\frac{5}{8} \times 12 = \frac{60}{8} = 7\frac{4}{8} = 7\frac{1}{2}$

n. $\frac{4}{9} \times 21 = \frac{84}{9} = 9\frac{3}{9} = 9\frac{1}{3}$

o. $\frac{5}{12} \times 10 = \frac{50}{12} = 4\frac{2}{12} = 4\frac{1}{6}$

p. $\frac{5}{6} \times 9 = \frac{45}{6} = 7\frac{3}{6} = 7\frac{1}{2}$

q. $\frac{3}{10} \times 16 = \frac{48}{10} = 4\frac{8}{10} = 4\frac{4}{5}$

r. $\frac{7}{12} \times 26 = \frac{182}{12} = 15\frac{2}{12} = 15\frac{1}{6}$

APPLICATIONS

Write multiplication equations:

1. Mother bought 5 pounds of meat.
   She cooked $\frac{2}{3}$ of the meat she bought.
   How much meat did she cook? $\frac{2}{3} \times 5 = \frac{10}{3} = 3\frac{1}{3}$ lb.

2. The capacity of the gas tank in your car is 15 gallons.
   It is full to $\frac{3}{4}$ of its capacity.
   How many gallons of gas are in the tank? $\frac{3}{4} \times 15 = \frac{45}{4} = 11\frac{1}{4}$

3. John works 40 hours a week.
   Last week, he only worked $\frac{2}{3}$ of his regular schedule.
   How many hours did he work last week? $\frac{2}{3} \times 40 = \frac{80}{3} = 26\frac{2}{3}$

4. Mr. Smith, the farmer, owns 27 ares of land.
   He grows corn on $\frac{3}{10}$ of his land.
   How many acres of land are used for corn? $\frac{3}{10} \times 27 = \frac{81}{10} = 8\frac{1}{10}$

5. You had $19.
   You spend $\frac{4}{5}$ of your money on books.
   How much did you spend? $\frac{4}{5} \times \$19 = \$\frac{76}{5} = \$15.20$

© Copyright by L. George Saad

Level 15

17   A MIXED NUMBER X A WHOLE NUMBER

Example 1.

Sue bought $2\frac{4}{5}$ yards of material for $3 a yard.

How much did she pay?

Discussion:

The situation calls for the multiplication $2\frac{4}{5}$ x 3.

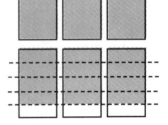

• You may find the answer in three steps:

     a. $2 \times 3 = 6$

     b. $\frac{4}{5} \times 3 = \frac{12}{5} = 2\frac{2}{5}$

     c. $6 + 2\frac{4}{5} = 8\frac{2}{5}$ She paid $8.40.

• You may also put the three steps together.

     $2\frac{4}{5}$ x 3 $= 6\frac{12}{5} = 8\frac{12}{5}$ She paid $8.40.

Example 2.

A farmer used a 5-bushel container to measure his corn.

He filled the container 7 times, and then filled it to $\frac{3}{4}$ of its capacity.

How many bushels of corn did he have?

Discussion:

The situation calls for the multiplication $7\frac{3}{4}$ x 5.

• You may find the answer in three steps:

     a. $7 \times 5 = 35$

     b. $\frac{3}{4} \times 5 = \frac{15}{4} = 3\frac{3}{4}$

     c. $35 + 3\frac{3}{4} = 38\frac{3}{4}$ He had $38\frac{3}{4}$ bushels.

• You may also put the three steps together:

     $7\frac{3}{4}$ x 5 $= 35\frac{15}{4} = 38\frac{3}{4}$ He had $38\frac{3}{4}$ bushels.

Example 3.

Multiply: $2\frac{5}{6}$ x 7

• In three steps

     a. $2 \times 7 = 14$

     b. $\frac{5}{6} \times 7 = \frac{35}{6} = 5\frac{5}{6}$

     c. $14 + 5\frac{5}{6} = 19\frac{5}{6}$

• In one step:

     $2\frac{5}{6}$ x 7 $= 14\frac{35}{6} = 19\frac{5}{6}$

Example 4.

Multiply: $5\frac{3}{8}$ x 6

• In three steps:

     a. $5 \times 6 = 30$

     b. $\frac{3}{8} \times 6 = \frac{18}{8} = 2\frac{2}{8} = 2\frac{1}{4}$

     c. $30 + 2\frac{1}{4} = 32\frac{1}{4}$

• In one step:

     $5\frac{3}{8}$ x 6 $= 30\frac{18}{8} = 32\frac{2}{8} = 32\frac{1}{4}$

© Copyright by L. George Saad

1. Multiply in three steps:

   a. $3\frac{2}{3} \times 5$

   $$\frac{3 \times 5 = 15}{\frac{2}{3} \times 5 = \frac{10}{3} = 3\frac{1}{3}}$$
   $$15 + 3\frac{1}{3} = 18\frac{1}{3}$$

   b. $5\frac{1}{4} \times 6$

   $$\frac{5 \times 6 = 30}{\frac{1}{4} \times 6 = \frac{6}{4} = 1\frac{1}{2}}$$
   $$30 + 1\frac{1}{2} = 31\frac{1}{2}$$

   c. $4\frac{3}{8} \times 7$

   $$\frac{4 \times 7 = 28}{\frac{3}{8} \times 7 = \frac{21}{8} = 2\frac{5}{8}}$$
   $$28 + 2\frac{5}{8} = 30\frac{5}{8}$$

   d. $2\frac{5}{6} \times 8$

   $$\frac{2 \times 8 = 16}{\frac{5}{6} \times 8 = \frac{40}{6} = 6\frac{2}{3}}$$
   $$16 + 6\frac{2}{3} = 22\frac{2}{3}$$

2. Multiply in one step:

   a. $4\frac{2}{7} \times 3 = 12\frac{6}{7}$

   b. $3\frac{2}{9} \times 4 = 12\frac{8}{9}$

   c. $5\frac{1}{8} \times 7 = 35\frac{7}{8}$

   d. $8\frac{3}{8} \times 2 = 16\frac{6}{8} = 16\frac{3}{4}$

   e. $5\frac{2}{3} \times 6 = 30\frac{12}{3} = 34$

   f. $7\frac{3}{4} \times 8 = 56\frac{24}{4} = 62$

   g. $8\frac{2}{5} \times 10 = 80\frac{20}{5} = 84$

   h. $2\frac{3}{7} \times 28 = 56\frac{84}{7} = 68$

   i. $4\frac{2}{3} \times 5 = 20\frac{10}{3} = 23\frac{1}{3}$

   j. $9\frac{2}{5} \times 6 = 54\frac{12}{5} = 56\frac{2}{5}$

APPLICATIONS

1. Don spent $18.
   Sam spent $1\frac{3}{4}$ times as much as Don.
   How much did Sam spend?

   $$1\frac{3}{4} \times 18 = 18\frac{54}{4} = 31\frac{1}{2} \text{ dollars}$$

2. Road A is 12 miles long.
   Road B is $2\frac{4}{5}$ as long as A.
   How long is road B?

   $$2\frac{4}{5} \times 12 = 24\frac{48}{5} = 33\frac{3}{5} \text{ miles}$$

3. Tom is 7 years old.
   His mother is $4\frac{2}{3}$ times as old as Tom.
   How old is the mother?

   $$4\frac{2}{3} \times 7 = 28\frac{14}{3} = 32\frac{2}{3} \text{ years}$$

4. What number is $3\frac{1}{2}$ times as large as 25?

   $$3\frac{1}{2} \times 25 = 75\frac{25}{2} = 87\frac{1}{2}$$

© Copyright by L. George Saad

EXERCISES

Multiply:

a. $\frac{1}{5}$ x 4 $= \frac{4}{5}$

b. $\frac{1}{3}$ x 2 $= \frac{2}{3}$

c. $\frac{1}{3}$ x 15 $= \frac{15}{3} = 5$

d. $\frac{1}{5}$ x 30 $= \frac{30}{5} = 6$

e. $\frac{1}{2}$ x 17 $= \frac{17}{2} = 8\frac{1}{2}$

f. $\frac{1}{7}$ x 30 $= \frac{30}{7} = 4\frac{2}{7}$

g. $\frac{2}{7}$ x 5 $= \frac{10}{7} = 1\frac{3}{7}$

h. $\frac{5}{8}$ x 13 $= \frac{65}{8} = 8\frac{1}{8}$

i. $\frac{2}{9}$ x 15 $= \frac{30}{9} = 3\frac{3}{9} = 3\frac{1}{3}$

j. $\frac{9}{14}$ x 10 $= \frac{90}{14} = 6\frac{6}{14} = 6\frac{3}{7}$

k. $5\frac{1}{3}$ x 2 $= 10\frac{2}{3}$

l. $3\frac{1}{5}$ x 4 $= 12\frac{4}{5}$

m. $4\frac{5}{6}$ x 12 $= 48\frac{60}{6} = 58$

n. $2\frac{2}{3}$ x 9 $= 18\frac{18}{3} = 24$

APPLICATIONS

1. Mr. Smith owns 14 acres of land.
   He grows tomatoes on $\frac{1}{3}$ of his land.
   How much land is planted tomatoes?

   $\frac{1}{3}$ x 14 $= \frac{14}{3} = 4\frac{2}{3}$ acres.

2. In the library, there are 900 books.
   $\frac{3}{10}$ of the books are in foreign languages.
   How many books are in foreign languages?

   $\frac{3}{10}$ x 900 = 270

3. During the summer, a family pays $52
   monthly for electricity.
   During the winter, the monthly payment is
   $1\frac{2}{5}$ times as much as that during the summer.
   How much is the winter monthly payment?

   $1\frac{2}{5}$ x 52 $= 52\frac{104}{5} = 72\frac{4}{5}$

   The payment is $72.80

4. The population of a village is 840 people.
   $\frac{2}{5}$ of the population is men, $\frac{3}{7}$ of the population
   is women and the rest is children.
   a. How many men are there?
   b. How many women are there?

   a. $\frac{2}{5}$ x 840 = 336

   b. $\frac{3}{7}$ x 840 = 360

© Copyright by L. George Saad

EXERCISES

Multiply:

a. $\frac{1}{9} \times 7 = \frac{7}{9}$ b. $\frac{1}{6} \times 5 = \frac{5}{6}$

c. $\frac{1}{2} \times 24 = \frac{24}{2} = 12$ d. $\frac{1}{4} \times 68 = \frac{68}{4} = 17$

e. $\frac{1}{4} \times 29 = \frac{29}{4} = 7\frac{1}{4}$ f. $\frac{1}{8} \times 75 = \frac{75}{8} = 9\frac{3}{8}$

g. $\frac{4}{5} \times 17 = \frac{68}{5} = 13\frac{3}{5}$ h. $\frac{2}{9} \times 40 = \frac{80}{9} = 8\frac{8}{9}$

i. $\frac{7}{10} \times 16 = \frac{112}{10} = 11\frac{2}{10} = 11\frac{1}{5}$ j. $\frac{5}{8} \times 12 = \frac{60}{8} = 7\frac{4}{8} = 7\frac{1}{2}$

k. $5\frac{2}{7} \times 3 = 15\frac{6}{7}$ l. $4\frac{2}{9} \times 4 = 16\frac{8}{9}$

m. $5\frac{3}{4} \times 8 = 40\frac{24}{4} = 46$ n. $3\frac{7}{8} \times 16 = 48\frac{112}{8} = 62$

APPLICATIONS

1. A school has 720 students.
   $\frac{3}{5}$ of the student body is boys.
   How many girls are in the school. $\frac{2}{5} \times 720 = 288$

2. A family's monthly income is $1022.
   $\frac{3}{8}$ of the income is spent on food, and
   $\frac{3}{10}$ of the income on rent.
   a. How much does food cost?
   b. How much is rent?

   a. $\frac{3}{8} \times 1022 = \frac{3066}{8} = 383\frac{2}{8} = \$383.25$
   b. $\frac{3}{10} \times 1022 = \frac{3066}{10} = 306\frac{6}{10} = \$306.60$

3. Three partners own 434 acres of land.
   One partner owns $\frac{2}{5}$ the land, and another
   owns $\frac{3}{8}$ the land.
   a. How many acres does the first own?
   b. How many acres does the second own?

   a. $\frac{2}{5} \times 434 = \frac{868}{5} = 173\frac{3}{5}$
   b. $\frac{3}{8} \times 434 = \frac{1302}{8} = 162\frac{6}{8} = 162\frac{3}{4}$

4. Jim bought a car for $1405.
   He paid $\frac{3}{10}$ of the price, and agreed to
   pay the rest in 10 equal payments.
   How much was each payment?

   a. $\frac{7}{10} \times 1405 = \frac{9835}{10} = 938.5$
   b. $983.5 \div 10 = 98.35$ dollars

© Copyright by L. George Saad   Level 15

Date _____

Example 1.

The figure is divided into halves.

One half is cut into 3 equal parts,

and 1 part is shaded.

$\frac{1}{3}$ of $\frac{1}{2}$ of the figure is shaded.

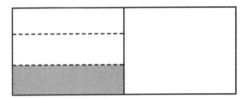

- You may say that $\frac{1}{2}$ is taken $\frac{1}{3}$ of one time.
- The shaded area is $\frac{1}{3} \times \frac{1}{2}$ of the whole figure.

Example 2.

The figure is divided into fourths.

One fourth is cut into 5 equal parts.

and 2 parts are shaded.

$\frac{2}{5}$ of $\frac{1}{4}$ of the figure is shaded.

- You may say that $\frac{1}{4}$ is taken $\frac{2}{5}$ of one time.
- The shaded area is $\frac{2}{5} \times \frac{1}{4}$ of the whole figure.

Example 3.

The figure is divided into fifths.

Two fifths are cut into 4 equal parts,

and 1 part is shaded.

$\frac{1}{4}$ of $\frac{2}{5}$ of the figure is shaded.

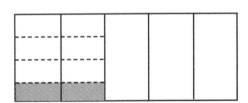

- You may say that $\frac{2}{5}$ is taken $\frac{1}{4}$ of one time.
- The shaded area is $\frac{1}{4} \times \frac{2}{5}$ of the whole figure.

Example 4.

The figure is divided into thirds.

Two thirds are cut into 5 equal parts,

and 4 parts are shaded.

$\frac{4}{5}$ of $\frac{2}{3}$ of the figure is shaded.

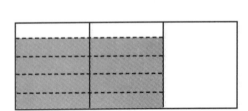

- You may say that $\frac{2}{3}$ is taken $\frac{4}{5}$ of one time.
- The shaded area is $\frac{4}{5} \times \frac{2}{3}$ of the whole figure.

© Copyright by L. George Saad

APPLICATIONS

In each question, the figure is divided into equal parts, and then one part (or more) is divided into equal parts.

Write the multiplication that shows what fraction of the figure is shaded.

a.

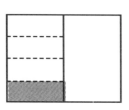

$$\frac{1}{4} \times \frac{1}{2}$$

b.

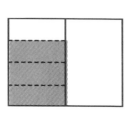

$$\frac{3}{4} \times \frac{1}{2}$$

c.

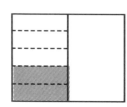

$$\frac{2}{5} \times \frac{1}{2}$$

d.

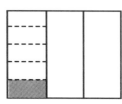

$$\frac{1}{5} \times \frac{1}{3}$$

e.

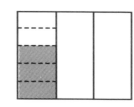

$$\frac{3}{5} \times \frac{1}{3}$$

f.

$$\frac{3}{5} \times \frac{2}{3}$$

g.

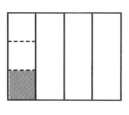

$$\frac{1}{3} \times \frac{1}{4}$$

h.

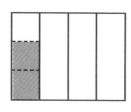

$$\frac{2}{3} \times \frac{1}{4}$$

i.

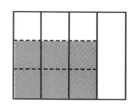

$$\frac{2}{3} \times \frac{3}{4}$$

j.

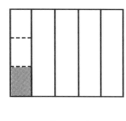

$$\frac{1}{3} \times \frac{1}{5}$$

k.

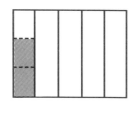

$$\frac{2}{3} \times \frac{1}{5}$$

l.

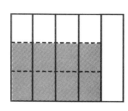

$$\frac{2}{3} \times \frac{4}{5}$$

© Copyright by L. George Saad

Level 15

19   A FRACTIONAL UNIT X A FRACTIONAL UNIT

Example 1.

The figure is divided into thirds.

$\frac{1}{2}$ x $\frac{1}{3}$ of the figure is shaded.

What fraction of the whole is shaded?

- Divide each of the other thirds into 2 equal parts.
- The whole becomes 2 rows with 3 parts in each row.
  The whole becomes 2 x 3 = 6 equal parts.
- $\frac{1}{6}$ of the whole is shaded.   You write the equation: $\frac{1}{2}$ x $\frac{1}{3}$ = $\frac{1}{2 \times 3}$ = $\frac{1}{6}$

Example 2.

The figure is divided into halves.

$\frac{1}{3}$ x $\frac{1}{2}$ of the figure is shaded.

What fraction of the whole is shaded?

- Divide the other half into 3 equal parts.
- The whole becomes 3 x 2 = 6 equal parts.
- $\frac{1}{6}$ of the whole is shaded.

You write the equation: $\frac{1}{3}$ x $\frac{1}{2}$ = $\frac{1}{3 \times 2}$ = $\frac{1}{6}$

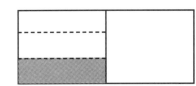

Example 3.

The figure is divided into fifths, and

$\frac{1}{3}$ x $\frac{1}{5}$ of the figure is shaded.

What fraction of the whole is shaded?

- Divide each of the other fifths into 3 equal parts.
- The whole becomes 3 x 5 = 15 equal parts.
- $\frac{1}{15}$ of the whole is shaded.

$\frac{1}{3}$ x $\frac{1}{5}$ = $\frac{1}{3 \times 5}$ = $\frac{1}{15}$

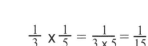

Example 4.

Show that $\frac{1}{5}$ x $\frac{1}{4}$ is the same as $\frac{1}{5 \times 4}$.

Solution:

- The shaded area is $\frac{1}{5}$ x $\frac{1}{4}$ of the whole.
- Divide each of the other fourths into 5 equal parts.
- The whole becomes (5 x 4) equal parts.
- One of these parts is shaded.
  The shaded area is $\frac{1}{5 \times 4}$ of the figure

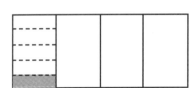

$\frac{1}{5}$ x $\frac{1}{4}$ = $\frac{1}{5 \times 4}$

Level 15

© Copyright by L. George Saad

APPLICATIONS

1. In each question, the figure is divided into equal parts, and then one part is divided into equal parts.

Write the multiplication equation that shows what fraction of the figure is shaded.

a.

$$\frac{1}{3} \times \frac{1}{2} = \frac{1}{3 \times 2} = \frac{1}{6}$$

b.
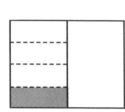

$$\frac{1}{4} \times \frac{1}{2} = \frac{1}{4 \times 2} = \frac{1}{8}$$

c.
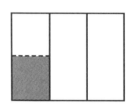

$$\frac{1}{2} \times \frac{1}{3} = \frac{1}{2 \times 3} = \frac{1}{6}$$

d.
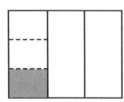

$$\frac{1}{3} \times \frac{1}{3} = \frac{1}{3 \times 3} = \frac{1}{9}$$

e.
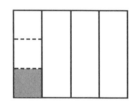

$$\frac{1}{3} \times \frac{1}{4} = \frac{1}{3 \times 4} = \frac{1}{12}$$

f.
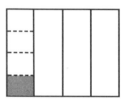

$$\frac{1}{4} \times \frac{1}{4} = \frac{1}{4 \times 4} = \frac{1}{16}$$

g.
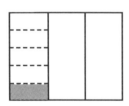

$$\frac{1}{5} \times \frac{1}{3} = \frac{1}{5 \times 3} = \frac{1}{15}$$

h.
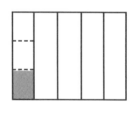

$$\frac{1}{3} \times \frac{1}{5} = \frac{1}{3 \times 5} = \frac{1}{15}$$

i.
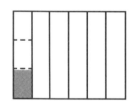

$$\frac{1}{3} \times \frac{1}{6} = \frac{1}{3 \times 6} = \frac{1}{18}$$

2. Write the answer:

a. $\frac{1}{3} \times \frac{1}{4} = \frac{1}{12}$

b. $\frac{1}{5} \times \frac{1}{2} = \frac{1}{10}$

c. $\frac{1}{3} \times \frac{1}{5} = \frac{1}{15}$

d. $\frac{1}{2} \times \frac{1}{7} = \frac{1}{14}$

e. $\frac{1}{5} \times \frac{1}{4} = \frac{1}{20}$

f. $\frac{1}{6} \times \frac{1}{5} = \frac{1}{30}$

g. $\frac{1}{4} \times \frac{1}{7} = \frac{1}{28}$

h. $\frac{1}{10} \times \frac{1}{5} = \frac{1}{50}$

i. $\frac{1}{3} \times \frac{1}{10} = \frac{1}{30}$

j. $\frac{1}{5} \times \frac{1}{8} = \frac{1}{40}$

k. $\frac{1}{10} \times \frac{1}{10} = \frac{1}{100}$

l. $\frac{1}{10} \times \frac{1}{20} = \frac{1}{200}$

m. $\frac{1}{5} \times \frac{1}{11} = \frac{1}{55}$

n. $\frac{1}{13} \times \frac{1}{7} = \frac{1}{91}$

o. $\frac{1}{25} \times \frac{1}{20} = \frac{1}{500}$

© Copyright by L. George Saad

Level 15

20 A FRACTION X A FRACTIONAL UNIT

Example 1.

The figure is divided into halves, and
1 half is divided into 4 equal parts.
$\frac{3}{4}$ x $\frac{1}{2}$ of the figure is shaded.
What fraction of the figure is shaded?

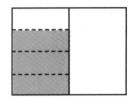

Discussion:

Divide the other half into 4 equal parts.

- The whole is now made of 4 rows of parts, with 2 parts in each row.
  The whole is made of (4 x 2) equal parts.
- The shaded area is 3 of these parts.
  The shaded area is $\frac{3}{4 \times 2} = \frac{3}{8}$ of the whole.

Example 2.

The figure is divided into thirds.
1 third is divided into 5 equal parts.
$\frac{4}{5}$ x $\frac{1}{3}$ of the figure is shaded.
What fraction of the figure is shaded?

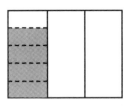

Discussion:

Divide each of the other 2 thirds into 5 equal parts.

- The whole is now made of 5 rows of parts, with 3 parts in each row.
  The whole is made of (5 x 3) equal parts.
- The shaded area is 4 of these parts.
  The shaded area is $\frac{4}{5 \times 3} = \frac{4}{15}$ of the whole.

Example 3.

The figure is divided into fifths.
1 fifth is divided into 3 equal parts.
$\frac{2}{3}$ x $\frac{1}{5}$ of the figure is shaded.
What fraction of the figure is shaded?

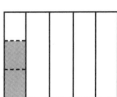

Discussion:

Divide each of the other fifths into 3 equal parts.

- In all, how many equal parts is the whole now made of ?
  Write the equation.   3 x 5 = 15
- How many of these parts are shaded?   2
- What fraction of the whole is shaded? $\frac{2}{15}$

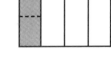

© Copyright by L. George Saad

APPLICATIONS

1. Show that $\frac{2}{5} \times \frac{1}{3}$ is the same as $\frac{2}{5 \times 3}$.

   $\frac{2}{5} \times \frac{1}{3}$ of the figure is shaded.
   We divide the other thirds into 5 equal parts.
   The whole is now made of (5 x 3) equal parts.
   2 parts are shaded. $\frac{2}{5 \times 3}$ of the figure is shaded.

   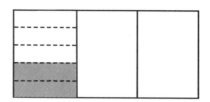

2. Show that $\frac{3}{4} \times \frac{1}{2}$ is the same as $\frac{3}{4 \times 2}$.

   $\frac{3}{4} \times \frac{1}{2}$ of the figure is shaded.
   We divide the other half into 4 equal parts.
   The whole is now made of (4 x 2) equal parts.
   3 parts are shaded. $\frac{3}{4 \times 2}$ of the figure is shaded.

   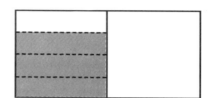

3. Mrs. Smith bought $\frac{1}{2}$ a gallon of milk.
   She used $\frac{3}{5}$ of the milk she bought.
   How much milk did she use?

   $\underline{\frac{3}{4} \times \frac{1}{2} = \frac{3}{8} \textbf{ gallon}}$

4. Your lawn is $\frac{1}{4}$ of one acre.
   You mowed $\frac{3}{5}$ of the lawn.
   How much land did you mow?

   $\underline{\frac{3}{5} \times \frac{1}{4} = \frac{3}{20} \textbf{ acre}}$

5. The school is $\frac{1}{2}$ of one mile from home.
   You walked $\frac{7}{8}$ of the distance.
   How far from home did you go?

   $\underline{\frac{7}{8} \times \frac{1}{2} = \frac{7}{16} \textbf{ mile}}$

EXERCISES

Write the answer:

a. $\frac{2}{5} \times \frac{1}{3} = \frac{2}{15}$ b. $\frac{2}{3} \times \frac{1}{5} = \frac{2}{15}$ c. $\frac{3}{5} \times \frac{1}{2} = \frac{3}{10}$

d. $\frac{3}{4} \times \frac{1}{2} = \frac{3}{8}$ e. $\frac{5}{6} \times \frac{1}{2} = \frac{5}{12}$ f. $\frac{7}{8} \times \frac{1}{3} = \frac{7}{24}$

g. $\frac{2}{3} \times \frac{1}{7} = \frac{2}{21}$ h. $\frac{3}{5} \times \frac{1}{4} = \frac{3}{20}$ i. $\frac{5}{9} \times \frac{1}{2} = \frac{5}{18}$

j. $\frac{3}{7} \times \frac{1}{4} = \frac{3}{28}$ k. $\frac{7}{10} \times \frac{1}{3} = \frac{7}{30}$ l. $\frac{3}{4} \times \frac{1}{10} = \frac{3}{40}$

m. $\frac{5}{9} \times \frac{1}{3} = \frac{5}{27}$ n. $\frac{3}{10} \times \frac{1}{10} = \frac{3}{100}$ o. $\frac{2}{5} \times \frac{1}{5} = \frac{2}{25}$

C

© Copyright by L. George Saad   **Level 15**

21   A FRACTION X A FRACTION

Example 1.

The figure is divided into fifths.

$\frac{2}{3}$ x $\frac{4}{5}$ of the figure is shaded.

What fraction of the figure is shaded?

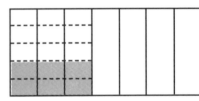

Discussion:

- Divide the other fifth into 3 equal parts.
- The whole is now made of 3 rows, with 5 parts in each row.

  The whole is made of 3 x 5 = 15 equal parts.
- The shaded area is made of 2 rows of parts.
- The shaded area is made of 2 x 4 = 8 parts.

  The shaded area is $\frac{8}{15}$ of the whole. You write the equation: $\frac{2}{3}$ x $\frac{4}{5}$ = $\frac{2 \times 4}{3 \times 5}$ = $\frac{8}{15}$

Example 2.

The whole is divided into sevenths.

$\frac{2}{5}$ x $\frac{3}{7}$ of the whole is shaded.

What fraction of the whole is shaded?

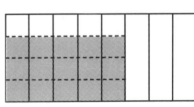

Discussion:

- Divide each of the other sevenths into 3 equal parts.
- How many parts are shaded?   <u>2 x 3 = 6</u>
- How many parts is the whole made of?   <u>5 x 7 = 35</u>
- What fraction of the whole is shaded? $\frac{6}{35}$

You can put the three steps together.   You write the equation: $\frac{2}{5}$ x $\frac{3}{7}$ = $\frac{2 \times 3}{5 \times 7}$ = $\frac{6}{35}$

Example 3.

Show that $\frac{3}{4}$ x $\frac{5}{8}$ is the same as $\frac{3 \times 5}{4 \times 8}$.

Solution:

- The shaded area is $\frac{3}{4}$ x $\frac{5}{8}$ of the figure.
- Divide each of the other eighths into 4 equal parts.
- The whole becomes (4 x 8) parts.
- The shaded area is (3 x 5) of these parts.
- The shaded area is $\frac{3 \times 5}{4 \times 8}$ of the figure.

The equation $\frac{3}{4}$ x $\frac{5}{8}$ = $\frac{3 \times 5}{4 \times 8}$ is true.

       © Copyright by L. George Saad

1. Show that $\frac{4}{5} \times \frac{2}{3}$ is the same as $\frac{4 \times 2}{5 \times 5}$.
   The shaded area is $\frac{4}{5} \times \frac{2}{3}$ of the figure.
   We divide the other third into 5 equal parts.
   The whole is now made of (5 x 3) equal parts.
   The shaded area is (4 x 2) of these parts.
   The shaded area is $\frac{4 \times 2}{5 \times 3}$ of the whole figure.

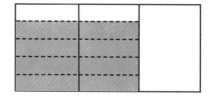

2. Show that $\frac{3}{4} \times \frac{3}{5}$ is the same as $\frac{3 \times 3}{4 \times 5}$.
   The shaded area is $\frac{3}{4} \times \frac{3}{5}$ of the figure.
   We divide each of the other fifths into 4 equal parts.
   The whole is now made of (4 x 5) equal parts.
   The shaded area is (3 x 3) of these parts.
   The shaded area is $\frac{3 \times 3}{4 \times 5}$ of the whole figure.

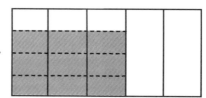

3. Mother bought $\frac{3}{4}$ lb. of meat.
   She cooked $\frac{3}{4}$ of the meat she bought.
   How much meat did she cook?

   $$\frac{3}{4} \times \frac{3}{4} = \frac{9}{16} \text{ lb.}$$

4. In a play, $\frac{3}{4}$ of the audience were adults
   and $\frac{3}{5}$ of the adults were men.
   What fraction of the audience was men?

   $$\frac{3}{5} \times \frac{3}{4} = \frac{9}{20}$$

5. Sue had $\frac{7}{8}$ yd. of fabric.
   She used $\frac{2}{3}$ of the fabric for a skirt.
   How much fabric did she use?

   $$\frac{2}{3} \times \frac{7}{8} = \frac{14}{24} = \frac{7}{12} \text{ yd.}$$

Write the answer:

a. $\frac{2}{3} \times \frac{4}{5} = \frac{8}{15}$ b. $\frac{3}{4} \times \frac{3}{5} = \frac{9}{20}$ c. $\frac{5}{8} \times \frac{3}{4} = \frac{15}{32}$

d. $\frac{5}{6} \times \frac{7}{8} = \frac{35}{48}$ e. $\frac{2}{5} \times \frac{2}{3} = \frac{4}{15}$ f. $\frac{3}{8} \times \frac{3}{5} = \frac{9}{40}$

g. $\frac{5}{7} \times \frac{3}{4} = \frac{15}{28}$ h. $\frac{5}{7} \times \frac{4}{9} = \frac{20}{63}$ i. $\frac{7}{8} \times \frac{5}{6} = \frac{35}{48}$

j. $\frac{3}{7} \times \frac{3}{4} = \frac{9}{28}$ k. $\frac{4}{9} \times \frac{5}{7} = \frac{20}{63}$ l. $\frac{9}{10} \times \frac{7}{8} = \frac{63}{80}$

m. $\frac{3}{8} \times \frac{7}{9} = \frac{21}{72}$ n. $\frac{2}{7} \times \frac{5}{9} = \frac{10}{63}$ o. $\frac{3}{5} \times \frac{9}{10} = \frac{27}{50}$

© Copyright by L. George Saad   **Level 15**

22 A FRACTION X A MIXED NUMBER

Example 1.

The figures are the same size.

Picture A represents $2\frac{1}{2}$ taken $\frac{3}{4}$ of one time.

The picture represents the multiplication $(\frac{3}{4} \times 2\frac{1}{2})$

What number is represented by the shaded area?

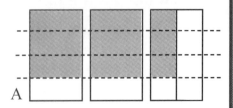

A

Discussion:

a. You may obtain the answer in three steps:

- $\frac{3}{4} \times 2 = \frac{6}{4} = 1\frac{2}{4}$
- $\frac{3}{4} \times \frac{1}{2} = \frac{3}{8}$
- $1\frac{2}{4} + \frac{3}{8} = 1\frac{4}{8} + \frac{3}{8} = 1\frac{7}{8}$

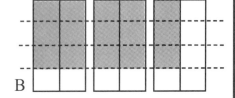

B

b. You also may do it another way:

- Divide the two whole figures into halves, as shown in picture B.
- The shaded area is now made of 5 halves taken $\frac{3}{4}$ of one time.
  The shaded area represents the multiplication: $(\frac{3}{4} \times \frac{5}{2})$.
- You also can measure the shaded area in eighths.
  The shaded area is made of 3 rows, with 5 eighths in each row.
  The shaded area is (3 x 5) eighths, which may be written: $\frac{3 \times 5}{4 \times 2} = \frac{15}{8}$
- In fractional form, you put all steps together:

$$\frac{3}{4} \times 2\frac{1}{2} = \frac{3}{4} \times \frac{5}{2} = \frac{3 \times 5}{4 \times 2} = \frac{15}{8} = 1\frac{7}{8}$$

It is obvious that the second method is shorter than the first.

Example 2.

The picture represents $1\frac{4}{5}$ taken $\frac{2}{3}$ of one time.

The picture represents the multiplication: $(\frac{2}{3} \times 1\frac{4}{5})$

What number is represented by the shaded area?

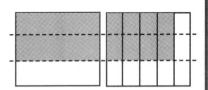

Discussion:

- Divide the whole figure into fifths.
- The shaded area is now made of 9 fifths, taken $\frac{2}{3}$ of one time.
  The shaded area represents the multiplication: $(\frac{2}{3} \times \frac{9}{5})$.
- You also can measure the shaded area in fifteenths.
  The shaded area is made of 2 rows, with 9 fifteenths in each row.
  The shaded area is (2 x 9) fifteenths, which may be written: $\frac{2 \times 9}{3 \times 5} = \frac{18}{15}$
- Putting all steps together, you write: $\frac{2}{3} \times 1\frac{4}{5} = \frac{2}{3} \times \frac{9}{5} = \frac{2 \times 9}{3 \times 5} = \frac{18}{15} = 1\frac{3}{15} = 1\frac{1}{5}$

Level 15

© Copyright by L. George Saad

APPLICATIONS

Study each picture:

1. a. What multiplication does the picture represent? $\frac{2}{3} \times 2\frac{1}{2}$
    b. Find the answer:
        $\frac{2}{3} \times 2\frac{1}{2} = \frac{2}{3} \times \frac{5}{2} = \frac{10}{6} = \frac{5}{3} = 1\frac{2}{3}$

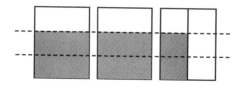

2. a. What multiplication does the picture represent? $\frac{3}{4} \times 1\frac{2}{5}$
    b. Find the answer:
        $\frac{3}{4} \times 1\frac{2}{5} = \frac{3}{4} \times \frac{7}{5} = \frac{21}{20} = 1\frac{1}{20}$

3. a. What multiplication does the picture represent? $\frac{4}{5} \times 2\frac{1}{3}$
    b. Find the answer:
        $\frac{4}{5} \times 2\frac{1}{3} = \frac{4}{5} \times \frac{7}{3} = \frac{28}{15} = 1\frac{13}{15}$

EXERCISES

Multiply:

a. $\frac{3}{8} \times 2\frac{3}{5} = \frac{3}{8} \times \frac{13}{5} = \frac{39}{40}$

b. $\frac{3}{7} \times 4\frac{1}{2} = \frac{3}{7} \times \frac{9}{2} = \frac{27}{14} = 1\frac{13}{14}$

c. $\frac{3}{5} \times 3\frac{1}{2} = \frac{3}{5} \times \frac{7}{2} = \frac{21}{10} = 2\frac{1}{10}$

d. $\frac{2}{3} \times 2\frac{1}{3} = \frac{2}{3} \times \frac{7}{3} = \frac{14}{9} = 1\frac{5}{9}$

e. $\frac{2}{3} \times 3\frac{1}{3} = \frac{2}{3} \times \frac{10}{3} = \frac{20}{9} = 2\frac{2}{9}$

f. $\frac{5}{8} \times 3\frac{1}{2} = \frac{5}{8} \times \frac{7}{2} = \frac{35}{16} = 2\frac{3}{16}$

g. $\frac{3}{4} \times 6\frac{3}{5} = \frac{3}{4} \times \frac{33}{5} = \frac{99}{20} = 4\frac{19}{20}$

h. $\frac{5}{6} \times 5\frac{2}{3} = \frac{5}{6} \times \frac{17}{3} = \frac{85}{18} = 4\frac{13}{18}$

i. $\frac{4}{5} \times 5\frac{2}{3} = \frac{4}{5} \times \frac{17}{3} = \frac{68}{15} = 4\frac{8}{15}$

j. $\frac{3}{5} \times 4\frac{3}{4} = \frac{3}{5} \times \frac{19}{4} = \frac{57}{20} = 2\frac{17}{20}$

k. $\frac{5}{8} \times 1\frac{3}{5} = \frac{5}{8} \times \frac{8}{5} = \frac{40}{40} = 1$

l. $\frac{5}{6} \times 1\frac{3}{4} = \frac{5}{6} \times \frac{7}{4} = \frac{35}{24} = 1\frac{11}{24}$

m. $\frac{3}{4} \times 4\frac{1}{2} = \frac{3}{4} \times \frac{9}{2} = \frac{27}{8} = 3\frac{3}{8}$

n. $\frac{2}{5} \times 3\frac{1}{2} = \frac{2}{5} \times \frac{7}{2} = \frac{14}{10} = 1\frac{4}{10} = 1\frac{2}{5}$

C

© Copyright by L. George Saad

Level 15

23   A MIXED NUMBER X A FRACTION

Example 1.

The figures are the same size.

Picture A represents $\frac{3}{4}$ taken $2\frac{1}{2}$ times.

Discussion:

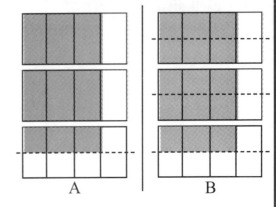

A   B

a. You may obtain the answer in three steps:

- $2 \times \frac{3}{4} = \frac{6}{4} = 1\frac{2}{4}$
- $\frac{1}{2} \times \frac{3}{4} = \frac{3}{8}$
- $1\frac{2}{4} + \frac{3}{8} = 1\frac{4}{8} + \frac{3}{8} = 1\frac{7}{8}$

b. Or you may do it another way:

- Divide the two figures into halves, as shown in picture B.

- The shaded area is now 3 fourths taken 5 half times.

  The shaded area represents the multiplication: $(\frac{5}{2} \times \frac{3}{4})$.

- You also can measure the shaded area in eighths.

  The shaded area is made of 5 rows, with 3 eighths in each row.

  The shaded area is made of (5 x 3) eighths, which may be written: $\frac{5 \times 3}{2 \times 4} = \frac{15}{8}$

- Putting all steps together, you write: $2\frac{1}{2} \times \frac{3}{4} = \frac{5}{2} \times \frac{3}{4} = \frac{5 \times 3}{2 \times 4} = \frac{15}{8} = 1\frac{7}{8}$

It is obvious that the second method is easier to use.

Example 2.

The picture represents $\frac{2}{3}$ taken $1\frac{4}{5}$ times.

The picture represents the multiplication $(1\frac{4}{5} \times \frac{2}{3})$.

What number is represented by the shaded area?

Discussion:

- Divide the whole figure into fifths.

- The shaded area is now made of 2 thirds taken 9 fifth times.

  The shaded area represents the multiplication $(\frac{9}{5} \times \frac{2}{3})$.

- You also can measure the shaded area in fifteenths.

  The shaded area is made of 9 rows, with 2 fifteenths in each row.

  The shaded area is made of (9 x 2) fifteenths, which may be written: $\frac{9 \times 2}{5 \times 3} = \frac{18}{15}$

- Putting all steps together, you write: $1\frac{4}{5} \times \frac{2}{3} = \frac{9}{5} \times \frac{2}{3} = \frac{9 \times 2}{5 \times 3} = \frac{18}{15} = 1\frac{3}{15} = 1\frac{1}{5}$

Level 15   © Copyright by L. George Saad

Study each picture:

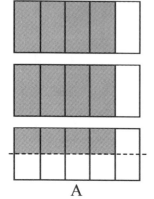
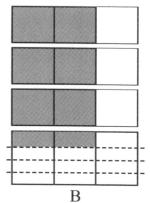

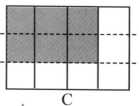

A   B   C

1. a. What multiplication does picture A represent? $\quad 2\frac{1}{2} \times \frac{4}{5}$

   b. Find the answer: $\quad 2\frac{1}{2} \times \frac{4}{5} = \frac{5}{2} \times \frac{4}{5} = \frac{20}{10} = 2$

2. a. What multiplication does picture B represent? $\quad 3\frac{1}{4} \times \frac{2}{3}$

   b. Find the answer: $\quad 3\frac{1}{4} \times \frac{2}{3} = \frac{13}{4} \times \frac{2}{3} = \frac{26}{12} = 2\frac{2}{12} = 2\frac{1}{6}$

3. a. What multiplication does picture C represent? $\quad 1\frac{2}{3} \times \frac{3}{4}$

   b. Find the answer: $\quad 1\frac{2}{3} \times \frac{3}{4} = \frac{5}{3} \times \frac{3}{4} = \frac{15}{12} = 1\frac{3}{12} = 1\frac{1}{4}$

EXERCISES

Multiply:

a. $2\frac{3}{5} \times \frac{3}{8} = \frac{13}{5} \times \frac{3}{8} = \frac{39}{40}$

b. $1\frac{2}{3} \times \frac{4}{7} = \frac{5}{3} \times \frac{4}{7} = \frac{20}{21}$

c. $1\frac{2}{5} \times \frac{2}{3} = \frac{7}{5} \times \frac{2}{3} = \frac{14}{15}$

d. $8\frac{1}{2} \times \frac{1}{3} = \frac{17}{2} \times \frac{1}{3} = \frac{17}{6} = 2\frac{5}{6}$

e. $1\frac{1}{8} \times \frac{3}{5} = \frac{9}{8} \times \frac{3}{5} = \frac{27}{40}$

f. $9\frac{3}{5} \times \frac{5}{8} = \frac{48}{5} \times \frac{5}{8} = \frac{240}{40} = 6$

g. $4\frac{1}{2} \times \frac{3}{7} = \frac{9}{2} \times \frac{3}{7} = \frac{27}{14} = 1\frac{13}{14}$

h. $7\frac{2}{5} \times \frac{3}{4} = \frac{37}{5} \times \frac{3}{4} = \frac{111}{20} = 5\frac{11}{20}$

i. $3\frac{2}{3} \times \frac{5}{6} = \frac{11}{3} \times \frac{5}{6} = \frac{55}{18} = 3\frac{1}{18}$

j. $3\frac{1}{2} \times \frac{3}{5} = \frac{7}{2} \times \frac{3}{5} = \frac{21}{10} = 2\frac{1}{10}$

k. $5\frac{2}{3} \times \frac{4}{5} = \frac{17}{3} \times \frac{4}{5} = \frac{68}{15} = 4\frac{8}{15}$

l. $4\frac{3}{4} \times \frac{3}{4} = \frac{19}{4} \times \frac{3}{4} = \frac{57}{16} = 3\frac{9}{16}$

© Copyright by L. George Saad

Level 15

24 A MIXED NUMBER X A MIXED NUMBER

Example:

The picture represents $2\frac{1}{5}$ taken $3\frac{1}{2}$ times.

The picture represents the multiplication $(3\frac{1}{2} \times 2\frac{1}{5})$

What number is represented by the shaded area?

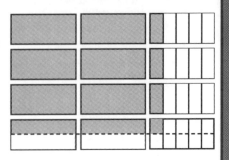

Solution 1.

You obtain the answer in 5 steps.

- $3 \times 2 = 6$
- $3 \times \frac{1}{5} = \frac{3}{5}$
- $\frac{1}{2} \times 2 = \frac{2}{2} = 1$
- $\frac{1}{2} \times \frac{1}{5} = \frac{1}{10}$
- $6 + \frac{3}{5} + 1 + \frac{1}{10} = 6 + \frac{6}{10} + 1 + \frac{1}{10} = 7\frac{7}{10}$

Solution 2.

Divide each figure into fifths, and then divide each set of 3 figures into 2 equal parts, as shown to the right.

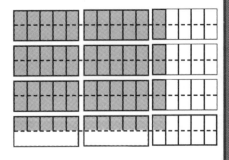

- The shaded area is now made of tenths.
  The shaded area is now made of 11 fifths taken
  7 half times, which may be written: $\frac{7}{2} \times \frac{11}{5}$
- The shaded area also may be measured in tenths.
  There are 7 rows, with 11 tenths in each row.
  There are (7 x 11) tenths, which may be written: $\frac{7 \times 11}{2 \times 5} = \frac{7 \times 11}{10} = \frac{77}{10}$
- Putting all steps together: $3\frac{1}{2} \times 2\frac{1}{5} = \frac{7}{2} \times \frac{11}{5} = \frac{7 \times 11}{2 \times 5} = \frac{77}{10} = 7\frac{7}{10}$

Examples:

$$5\frac{2}{3} \times 1\frac{3}{4} = \frac{17}{3} \times \frac{7}{4} = \frac{17 \times 7}{3 \times 4} = \frac{119}{12} = 9\frac{11}{12}$$

$$2\frac{3}{4} \times 3\frac{1}{2} = \frac{11}{4} \times \frac{7}{2} = \frac{11 \times 7}{4 \times 2} = \frac{77}{8} = 9\frac{5}{8}$$

$$4\frac{2}{3} \times 4\frac{1}{2} = \frac{14}{3} \times \frac{9}{2} = \frac{14 \times 9}{3 \times 2} = \frac{126}{6} = 21$$

$$7\frac{1}{2} \times 2\frac{3}{5} = \frac{15}{2} \times \frac{13}{5} = \frac{15 \times 13}{2 \times 5} = \frac{195}{10} = 19\frac{1}{2}$$

$$6\frac{2}{3} \times 2\frac{1}{3} = \frac{20}{3} \times \frac{7}{3} = \frac{20 \times 7}{3 \times 3} = \frac{140}{9} = 15\frac{5}{9}$$

 © Copyright by L. George Saad

Multiply:

a. $3\frac{1}{2} \times 1\frac{1}{4} = \frac{7}{2} \times \frac{5}{4} = \frac{35}{8} = 4\frac{3}{8}$

b. $2\frac{1}{5} \times 4\frac{1}{2} = \frac{11}{5} \times \frac{9}{2} = \frac{99}{10} = 9.9$

c. $4\frac{1}{3} \times 1\frac{1}{4} = \frac{13}{3} \times \frac{5}{4} = \frac{65}{12} = 5\frac{5}{12}$

d. $1\frac{4}{5} \times 1\frac{3}{4} = \frac{9}{5} \times \frac{7}{4} = \frac{63}{20} = 3\frac{3}{20}$

e. $1\frac{3}{8} \times 2\frac{1}{2} = \frac{11}{8} \times \frac{5}{2} = \frac{55}{16} = 3\frac{7}{16}$

f. $3\frac{2}{3} \times 2\frac{1}{3} = \frac{11}{3} \times \frac{7}{3} = \frac{77}{9} = 8\frac{5}{9}$

g. $2\frac{1}{2} \times 7\frac{1}{5} = \frac{5}{2} \times \frac{36}{5} = \frac{180}{10} = 18$

h. $1\frac{2}{3} \times 4\frac{3}{4} = \frac{5}{3} \times \frac{19}{4} = \frac{95}{12} = 7\frac{11}{12}$

i. $3\frac{4}{7} \times 2\frac{4}{5} = \frac{25}{7} \times \frac{14}{5} = \frac{350}{35} = 10$

j. $3\frac{1}{2} \times 5\frac{3}{4} = \frac{7}{2} \times \frac{23}{4} = \frac{161}{8} = 20\frac{1}{8}$

k. $2\frac{1}{4} \times 3\frac{1}{2} = \frac{9}{4} \times \frac{7}{2} = \frac{63}{8} = 7\frac{7}{8}$

l. $8\frac{1}{3} \times 1\frac{3}{7} = \frac{25}{3} \times \frac{10}{7} = \frac{250}{21} = 11\frac{19}{21}$

m. $3\frac{2}{3} \times 3\frac{1}{2} = \frac{11}{3} \times \frac{7}{2} = \frac{77}{6} = 12\frac{5}{6}$

n. $2\frac{4}{5} \times 3\frac{2}{3} = \frac{14}{5} \times \frac{11}{3} = \frac{154}{15} = 10\frac{4}{15}$

o. $4\frac{1}{2} \times 3\frac{4}{5} = \frac{9}{2} \times \frac{19}{5} = \frac{171}{10} = 17\frac{1}{10}$

p. $4\frac{2}{3} \times 1\frac{2}{3} = \frac{14}{3} \times \frac{5}{3} = \frac{70}{9} = 7\frac{7}{9}$

1. Bob covers $5\frac{1}{2}$ miles per hour on his bicycle.
   How many miles does he cover in $3\frac{3}{4}$ hours? $3\frac{3}{4} \times 5\frac{1}{2} = \frac{15}{4} \times \frac{11}{2} = \frac{165}{8} = 20\frac{5}{8}$ miles

2. A metal bar is $3\frac{2}{3}$ feet long.
   It weighs $1\frac{1}{8}$ lb. per foot.
   How much does the bar weigh? $3\frac{2}{3} \times 1\frac{1}{8} = \frac{11}{3} \times \frac{9}{8} = \frac{99}{24} = 4\frac{1}{8}$ lbs.

3. Jack's lawn is $1\frac{2}{5}$ acres.
   He uses $25\frac{1}{2}$ lb. of seed for one acre.
   How much seed is needed for the whole lawn? $1\frac{2}{5} \times 25\frac{1}{2} = \frac{7}{5} \times \frac{51}{2} = 35.7$ lbs.

4. $A = 3\frac{1}{2} \times 4\frac{1}{3}$
   B is 4 times A.
   What number is B?
   $A = 3\frac{1}{2} \times 4\frac{1}{3} = \frac{7}{2} \times \frac{13}{3} = \frac{91}{6} = 15\frac{1}{6}$
   $B = 4 \times 15\frac{1}{6} = 60\frac{4}{6} = 60\frac{2}{3}$

5. Find the answer:
   $(8\frac{3}{4} \times 2\frac{1}{3}) - (5\frac{2}{3} \times 1\frac{1}{4})$
   a. $8\frac{3}{4} \times 2\frac{1}{3} = \frac{35}{4} \times \frac{7}{3} = \frac{245}{12} = 20\frac{5}{12}$
   b. $5\frac{2}{3} \times 1\frac{1}{4} = \frac{17}{3} \times \frac{5}{4} = \frac{85}{12} = 7\frac{1}{12}$
   c. $20\frac{5}{12} - 7\frac{1}{12} = 13\frac{4}{12} = 13\frac{1}{3}$

© Copyright by L. George Saad

25 MULTIPLYING DECIMALS

Example.

To multiply 0.7 x 0.3, you first write 0.7 and 0.3 as common fractions:

$$0.7 \times 0.3 = \frac{7}{10} \times \frac{3}{10} = \frac{21}{100} = 0.21$$

Similarly:

a. $0.2 \times 0.4 = \frac{2}{10} \times \frac{4}{10} = \frac{8}{100} = 0.08$

b. $0.3 \times 0.07 = \frac{3}{10} \times \frac{7}{100} = \frac{21}{1000} = 0.021$

c. $0.6 \times 0.17 = \frac{6}{10} \times \frac{17}{100} = \frac{102}{1000} = 0.102$

d. $0.07 \times 0.19 = \frac{7}{100} \times \frac{19}{100} = \frac{133}{10000} = 0.0133$

Note:

Without changing into common fractions, you could predict where the decimal point in the answer would be:

a. For 0.2 x 0.4, the answer is in <u>hundredths.</u>   0.2 x 0.4   = <u>0.08</u>

b. For 0.3 x 0.07, the answer is in <u>thousandths.</u>   0.3 x 0.07 = <u>0.021</u>

c. For 0.6 x 0.17, the answer is in <u>thousandths.</u>   0.6 x 0.17 = <u>0.102</u>

d. For 0.07 x 0.19, the answer is in <u>10 thousandths</u>.   0.07 x 0.19 = <u>0.0133</u>

EXERCISES

1. Multiply as common fractions:

a. $0.4 \times 0.2 = \frac{4}{10} \times \frac{2}{10} = \frac{8}{100} = 0.08$

b. $0.03 \times 0.2 = \frac{3}{100} \times \frac{2}{10} = \frac{6}{1000} = 0.006$

c. $0.25 \times 0.7 = \frac{25}{100} \times \frac{7}{10} = \frac{175}{1000} = 0.175$

d. $0.025 \times 0.36 = \frac{25}{1000} \times \frac{36}{100} = \frac{900}{10000} = 0.00090$

2. Write the answer:

a. 0.2 x 0.7   = <u>0.14</u>   b. 0.3 x 0.2   = <u>0.06</u>

c. 0.15 x 0.2   = <u>0.030</u>   d. 0.6 x 0.09 = <u>0.054</u>

e. 0.09 x 0.02 = <u>0.0018</u>   f. 0.02 x 0.4 = <u>0.008</u>

g. 0.16 x 0.05 = <u>0.0080</u>   h. 0.04 x 0.5 = <u>0.020</u>

© Copyright by L. George Saad

Example 3.

You bought 3.6 lb. of meat for $2.85 per pound.
How much did you pay?

$$
\begin{array}{r}
285 \\
\times\ 36 \\
\hline
1710 \\
855 \\
\hline
10260
\end{array}
$$

Discussion:

The situation calls for the multiplication: 3.6 x 2.85.

• You change into common fractions, and then multiply in the usual manner:

$$3.6 \times 2.85 = 3\tfrac{6}{10} \times 2\tfrac{85}{100} = \tfrac{36}{10} \times \tfrac{285}{100} = \tfrac{10260}{1000} = 10.260 \quad \text{You paid \$10.26}$$

• You do not have to do all this work.
The numerator of the answer is 36 x 285.
The denominator of the answer is 10 x 100.

Example 4.

Make the answer correct: 2.16 x 3.7 = 7992

$$
\begin{array}{r}
216 \\
\times\ 37 \\
\hline
1512 \\
648 \\
\hline
7992
\end{array}
$$

Discussion:

The answer has a fractional part. It is in thousandths.
In the answer there is a decimal point after 3 digits
from the right.

$$2.16 \times 3.7 = \underline{\ 7.992\ }$$

Example 5.

Multiply: 7.09 x 3.24

$$
\begin{array}{r}
709 \\
\times\ 324 \\
\hline
2836 \\
1418 \\
2127 \\
\hline
229716
\end{array}
$$

Discussion:

• Find the numerator in the answer: $\underline{\ 709 \times 324 = 229716\ }$
• Find the denominator: $\underline{\ 100 \times 100 = 10000\ }$
• How many decimal places are in the answer? $\underline{\ 4\ }$
• What is the answer? $7.09 \times 3.24 = \underline{\ 22.9716\ }$

EXERCISES

Make the answer correct:

a. 3.5 x 1.7 = 595 $\underline{\ 5.95\ }$ b. 1.2 x 35.3 = 4236 $\underline{\ 42.36\ }$

c. 2.64 x 2.8 = 7392 $\underline{\ 7.392\ }$ d. 2.75 x 0.9 = 2475 $\underline{\ 2.475\ }$

e. 76.1 x 3.4 = 25874 $\underline{\ 258.74\ }$ f. 36.4 x 2.5 = 9100 $\underline{\ 91.00\ }$

g. 3.74 x 0.25 = 9350 $\underline{\ 0.9350\ }$ h. 7.85 x 1.23 = 96555 $\underline{\ 9.6555\ }$

i. 28.42 x .09 = 25578 $\underline{\ 2.5578\ }$ j. 56.8 x 13.5 = 76680 $\underline{\ 766.80\ }$

k. 0.365 x 0.18 = 6570 $\underline{\ 0.06570\ }$ l. 0.961 x 0.23 = 22103 $\underline{\ 0.22103\ }$

© Copyright by L. George Saad

Level 15

EXERCISES

Multiply:

a. 3.7 x 2.3	b. 3.5 x 3.6	c. 1.3 x 3.5	d. 2.93 x 2.5
<u>8.51</u>	<u>12.60</u>	<u>4.55</u>	<u>7.325</u>
e. 4.6 x 5.55	f. 4.25 x 2.4	g. 6.43 x 4.7	h. 2.81 x 4.5
<u>25.530</u>	<u>10.200</u>	<u>30.221</u>	<u>12.645</u>
i. 14.5 x 0.38	j. 25.6 x 4.38	k. 9.85 x 2.54	l. 2.56 x 1.2
<u>5.510</u>	<u>112.128</u>	<u>25.019</u>	<u>3.072</u>
m. 3.78 x 9.61	n. 7.68 x 5.14	o. 5.316 x 2.8	p. 19.4 x 0.065
<u>36.3258</u>	<u>39.4752</u>	<u>14.8848</u>	<u>1.2610</u>
q. 0.471 x 0.21	r. 0.023 x 0.015	s. 0.168 x 0.95	t. 6.035 x 0.018
<u>0.09891</u>	<u>0.000345</u>	<u>0.15960</u>	<u>0.10863</u>

© Copyright by L. George Saad

APPLICATIONS

1. You drive for 3.6 hours at 52.7 miles per hour.
   How many miles did you cover?

   3.6 x 52.7 = 189.72

2. You bought 3.64 pounds of meat at $1.75 per pound.
   How much did you pay?

   3.64 x $ 1.75 = $6.37

3. Approximately, 1 mile is equivalent to 1.6 kilometers, and 1 kilometer is equivalent to 0.62 miles.

   a. How many miles are equivalent to 2.54 kilometers?

   2.54 x 0.62 = 1.5748

   b. How many kilometers are equivalent to in 3.6 miles?

   3.6 x 1.6 = 5.76

4. Approximately, 1 pound is equivalent to 0.45 kilogram, and 1 kilogram is equivalent to 2.2 pounds.

   a. How many pounds are equivalent to 8.5 kilograms?

   8.5 x 2.2 = 18.70

   b. How many kilograms are equivalent to 3.8 pounds?

   3.8 x 0.45 = 1.710

5. N = 109.4 - (53.75 x 0.8)
   What number is N?

   a. 53.75 x 0.8 = 43
   b. 109.4 - 43.0 = 66.4

6. A = (85.64 x 1.5) - 63.58
   What number is A?

   a. 85.64 x 1.5 = 128.46
   b. 128.46 - 63.58 = 64.88

© Copyright by L. George Saad

26 SIMPLIFYING THE MULTIPLICATION OF FRACTIONS

Example 1.

Multiply: $2\frac{4}{5} \times 3\frac{1}{3}$

Discussion:

- Part of the work you do is shown below.

$$2\frac{4}{5} \times 3\frac{1}{3} = \frac{14}{5} \times \frac{10}{3}$$

- Instead of multiplying 14 x 10 = 140, and 3 x 5 = 15, and then dividing 140 by 15, you can divide 10 by 5 and 5 by 5, and thus you get smaller numbers to work.

$$2\frac{4}{5} \times 3\frac{1}{3} = \frac{14}{5} \times \frac{10}{3} = \frac{14}{1} \times \frac{2}{3} = \frac{28}{3} = 9\frac{1}{3}$$

Example 2.

Multiply: $5\frac{5}{6} \times 2\frac{7}{10}$

Discussion:

- Change into improper fractions: $5\frac{5}{6} \times 2\frac{7}{10} = \frac{35}{6} \times \frac{27}{10}$
- Divide 35 and 10 by 5. You get: $\frac{7}{6} \times \frac{27}{2}$
- Divide 27 and 6 by 3. You get: $\frac{7}{2} \times \frac{9}{2}$
- You have obtained the smallest numbers.

Complete the work: $5\frac{5}{6} \times 2\frac{7}{10} = \frac{35}{6} \times \frac{27}{10} = \frac{7}{2} \times \frac{9}{2} = \frac{63}{4} = 15\frac{3}{4}$

Example 3.

Multiply: $\frac{12}{35} \times 3\frac{1}{8}$

Discussion:

- Change $3\frac{1}{8}$ into an improper fraction: $\frac{12}{35} \times \frac{25}{8}$
- Divide 25 and 35 by 5. The multiplication become $\frac{12}{7} \times \frac{5}{8}$.
- Divide 12 and 8 by 4. The multiplication becomes $\frac{3}{7} \times \frac{5}{2}$.

Complete the work: $\frac{12}{35} \times \frac{25}{8} = \frac{3}{7} \times \frac{5}{2} = \frac{15}{14} = 1\frac{1}{14}$

Example 4.

Multiply: $4\frac{7}{8} \times 3\frac{1}{9}$

Discussion:

- Change into improper fractions: $\frac{39}{8} \times \frac{28}{9}$
- Divide 39 and 9 by 3 and divide 28 and 8 by 4.

$$\frac{39}{8} \times \frac{28}{9} = \frac{13}{2} \times \frac{7}{3} = \frac{91}{6} = 15\frac{1}{6}$$

Level 15

© Copyright by L. George Saad

1. Simplify and then multiply:

a. $\frac{5}{14} \times \frac{21}{25} = \frac{1}{2} \times \frac{3}{5} = \frac{3}{10}$

b. $\frac{5}{6} \times \frac{8}{9} = \frac{5}{3} \times \frac{4}{9} = \frac{20}{27}$

c. $\frac{8}{15} \times \frac{35}{44} = \frac{2}{3} \times \frac{7}{11} = \frac{14}{33}$

d. $\frac{6}{7} \times \frac{14}{27} = \frac{2}{1} \times \frac{2}{9} = \frac{4}{9}$

e. $\frac{9}{10} \times \frac{5}{6} = \frac{3}{2} \times \frac{1}{2} = \frac{3}{4}$

f. $\frac{8}{9} \times \frac{15}{28} = \frac{2}{3} \times \frac{5}{7} = \frac{10}{21}$

g. $\frac{3}{16} \times 2\frac{2}{9} = \frac{3}{16} \times \frac{20}{9} = \frac{1}{4} \times \frac{5}{3} = \frac{5}{12}$

h. $\frac{4}{9} \times 13\frac{1}{2} = \frac{4}{9} \times \frac{27}{2} = \frac{2}{1} \times \frac{3}{1} = 6$

i. $3\frac{3}{4} \times \frac{4}{5} = \frac{15}{4} \times \frac{4}{5} = \frac{3}{1} \times \frac{1}{1} = 3$

j. $\frac{5}{6} \times 3\frac{3}{10} = \frac{5}{6} \times \frac{33}{10} = \frac{1}{2} \times \frac{11}{2} = 2\frac{3}{4}$

k. $8\frac{1}{4} \times 5\frac{1}{3} = \frac{33}{4} \times \frac{16}{3} = \frac{11}{1} \times \frac{4}{1} = 44$

l. $7\frac{1}{5} \times 3\frac{1}{3} = \frac{36}{5} \times \frac{10}{3} = \frac{12}{1} \times \frac{2}{1} = 24$

m. $6\frac{2}{5} \times 3\frac{3}{4} = \frac{32}{5} \times \frac{15}{4} = \frac{8}{1} \times \frac{3}{1} = 24$

n. $6\frac{1}{4} \times 2\frac{2}{5} = \frac{25}{4} \times \frac{12}{5} = \frac{5}{1} \times \frac{3}{1} = 15$

o. $4\frac{1}{5} \times 7\frac{1}{7} = \frac{21}{5} \times \frac{50}{7} = \frac{3}{1} \times \frac{10}{1} = 30$

p. $8\frac{2}{5} \times 2\frac{2}{9} = \frac{42}{5} \times \frac{20}{9} = \frac{14}{1} \times \frac{4}{3} = 18\frac{2}{3}$

2. Find the answer:

a. $24 - (2\frac{1}{2} \times 4\frac{2}{5})$

$2\frac{1}{2} \times 4\frac{2}{5} = \frac{5}{2} \times \frac{22}{5} = 11$

$24 - 11 = 13$

b. $5\frac{1}{3} + (4\frac{1}{5} \times 1\frac{1}{9})$

$4\frac{1}{5} \times 1\frac{1}{9} = \frac{21}{5} \times \frac{10}{9} = \frac{14}{3} = 4\frac{2}{3}$

$5\frac{1}{3} + 4\frac{2}{3} = 10$

c. $(2\frac{1}{4} \times 3\frac{1}{3}) \div 6$

$2\frac{1}{4} \times 3\frac{1}{3} = \frac{9}{4} \times \frac{10}{3} = \frac{15}{2} = 7\frac{1}{2}$

$7\frac{1}{2} \div 6 = \frac{15}{2} \div 6 = \frac{15}{12} = 1\frac{3}{12} = 1\frac{1}{4}$

d. $(4\frac{1}{2} - 1\frac{3}{5}) \times 2\frac{6}{7}$

$4\frac{1}{2} - 1\frac{3}{5} = 4\frac{5}{10} - 1\frac{6}{10} = 2\frac{9}{10}$

$2\frac{9}{10} \times 2\frac{6}{7} = \frac{29}{10} \times \frac{20}{7} = \frac{58}{7} = 8\frac{2}{7}$

© Copyright by L. George Saad

APPLICATIONS

1. a. What number is $4\frac{1}{2}$ more than $7\frac{1}{8}$?

    b. What number is $4\frac{1}{2}$ less than $7\frac{1}{8}$?

    a. $7\frac{1}{8} + 4\frac{1}{2} = 7\frac{1}{8} + 4\frac{4}{8} = 11\frac{5}{8}$

    b. $7\frac{1}{8} - 4\frac{1}{2} = 7\frac{1}{8} - 4\frac{4}{8} = 2\frac{5}{8}$

2. a. What number is $3\frac{2}{3}$ times as much as $2\frac{1}{4}$?

    b. $1\frac{2}{5}$ times N is 6. What number is N?

    a. $3\frac{2}{3} \times 2\frac{1}{4} = \frac{11}{3} \times \frac{9}{4} = \frac{99}{12} = 8\frac{3}{12} = 8\frac{1}{4}$

    b. $6 \div \frac{7}{5} = \frac{30}{5} \div \frac{7}{5} = \frac{30}{7} = 4\frac{2}{7}$

3. In a division exercise, the divisor is $2\frac{2}{3}$ and the quotient is $3\frac{3}{4}$. What number is the dividend?

    $2\frac{2}{3} \times 3\frac{3}{4} = \frac{8}{3} \times \frac{15}{4} = 10$

4. The product of two numbers is 9. One number is $5\frac{1}{2}$. What is the other number?

    $9 \div 5\frac{1}{2} = \frac{18}{2} \div \frac{11}{2} = \frac{18}{11} = 1\frac{7}{11}$

5. The sum of two numbers is $7\frac{2}{3}$. One number is $5\frac{3}{4}$. What is the other number?

    $7\frac{2}{3} - 5\frac{3}{4} = 7\frac{8}{12} - 5\frac{9}{12} = 1\frac{11}{12}$

6. The difference between two numbers is $5\frac{3}{10}$. The larger number is $9\frac{1}{5}$. Find the smaller number.

    $9\frac{1}{5} - 5\frac{3}{10} = 9\frac{2}{10} - 5\frac{3}{10} = 3\frac{9}{10}$

7. The difference between two numbers is $3\frac{3}{4}$. The smaller number is $6\frac{5}{6}$. Find the larger number.

    $6\frac{5}{6} + 3\frac{3}{4} = 6\frac{10}{12} + 3\frac{9}{12} = 10\frac{7}{12}$

8. N = $20\frac{1}{2} - (3\frac{1}{2} \times 4\frac{3}{4})$. What number is N?

    a. $3\frac{1}{2} \times 4\frac{3}{4} = \frac{7}{2} \times \frac{19}{4} = \frac{133}{8} = 16\frac{5}{8}$

    b. N = $20\frac{1}{2} - 16\frac{5}{8} = 20\frac{4}{8} - 16\frac{5}{8} = 3\frac{7}{8}$

9. A = (3.5 x 3.6) + (2.93 x 2.5) What number is A?

    A = 12.600 + 7.325 = 19.925

10. X = $(\frac{5}{6} + \frac{3}{4}) \times (6\frac{3}{4} - 4\frac{1}{2})$ What number is X?

    a. $\frac{5}{6} + \frac{3}{4} = \frac{10}{12} + \frac{9}{12} = \frac{19}{12} = 1\frac{7}{12}$

    b. $6\frac{3}{4} - 4\frac{1}{2} = 6\frac{3}{4} - 4\frac{2}{4} = 2\frac{1}{4}$

    c. X = $1\frac{7}{12} \times 2\frac{1}{4} = \frac{19}{12} \times \frac{9}{2} = \frac{57}{8} = 7\frac{1}{8}$

  © Copyright by L. George Saad

You know that:

$$\frac{7}{8} \times \frac{8}{7} = 1 \qquad\qquad \frac{9}{11} \times \frac{11}{9} = 1 \qquad\qquad \frac{13}{15} \times \frac{15}{13} = 1$$

$$\frac{100}{27} \times \frac{27}{100} = 1 \qquad\qquad 6 \times \frac{1}{6} = 1 \qquad\qquad 31 \times \frac{1}{31} = 1$$

Any two numbers whose product is 1 are called reciprocals and each is the reciprocal of the other.

Examples:

a. $\frac{6}{7} \times A = 1$. What number is A? $\qquad\qquad\qquad \underline{\frac{7}{6} = 1\frac{1}{6}}$

b. $1\frac{7}{8} \times N = 1$. What number is N? $\qquad\qquad\qquad \underline{\frac{8}{15}}$

c. $Y \times \frac{3}{5} = 1$. What number is Y? $\qquad\qquad\qquad \underline{\frac{5}{3} = 1\frac{2}{3}}$

EXERCISES

1. Find the reciprocal of each of the following:
   a. 5 $\quad\underline{\frac{1}{5}}\quad$ b. $\frac{3}{4}$ $\quad\underline{\frac{4}{3}}\quad$ c. $\frac{8}{17}$ $\quad\underline{\frac{7}{18}}$

   d. $10\frac{2}{3}$ $\quad\underline{\frac{3}{32}}\quad$ e. $5\frac{7}{8}$ $\quad\underline{\frac{8}{47}}\quad$ f. $9\frac{1}{2}$ $\quad\underline{\frac{2}{19}}$

2. a. The reciprocal of a number is $\frac{5}{7}$. What is the number? $\qquad\underline{\frac{7}{5}}$

   b. The reciprocal of a number is 3. What is the number? $\qquad\underline{\frac{1}{3}}$

3. a. Multiply: $4\frac{4}{5} \times 2\frac{2}{9}$
   b. Divide by $2\frac{2}{3}$.
   c. What is the reciprocal of the answer?

   a. $\frac{24}{5} \times \frac{20}{9} = \frac{32}{3} = 10\frac{2}{3}$
   b. $\frac{32}{3} \div \frac{8}{3} = \frac{32}{8} = 4$ $\qquad\underline{\frac{1}{4}}$

4. a. Subtract: $8\frac{1}{3} - 5\frac{1}{2}$
   b. Multiply by $2\frac{2}{3}$.
   c. What is the reciprocal of the answer?

   a. $8\frac{1}{3} - 5\frac{1}{2} = 8\frac{2}{6} - 5\frac{3}{6} = 2\frac{5}{6}$
   b. $2\frac{2}{3} \times 2\frac{5}{6} = \frac{8}{3} \times \frac{17}{6} = \frac{68}{9} = 7\frac{5}{9}$ $\quad\underline{\frac{9}{68}}$

5. a. Add: $2\frac{3}{4} + 1\frac{5}{6}$
   b. Multiply by $1\frac{3}{5}$.
   c. What is the reciprocal of the answer?

   a. $2\frac{3}{4} + 1\frac{5}{6} = 2\frac{9}{12} + 1\frac{10}{12} = 4\frac{7}{12}$
   b. $1\frac{3}{5} \times 4\frac{7}{12} = \frac{8}{5} \times \frac{55}{12} = \frac{22}{3} = 7\frac{1}{3}$ $\quad\underline{\frac{3}{22}}$

© Copyright by L. George Saad

Level 15

UNIT C TEST

1. The four figures are the same size.
   The set of figures is cut into 3 equal parts.
   a. Shade $(\frac{1}{3} \times 4)$

   b. Shade $(\frac{2}{3} \times 4)$

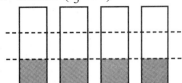 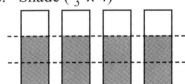

2. The three figures are the same size.
   The set of figures is cut into 2 equal parts.
   a. Shade $(\frac{1}{2} \times 3)$
   b. Show that $\frac{1}{2} \times 3$ is equal to 3 halves.
      We have 3 wholes. 1 half of each is shaded.
      3 halves are shaded.

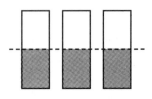

3. Multiply:
   a. $\frac{1}{3} \times 2 = \frac{2}{3}$

   b. $\frac{1}{2} \times 7 = \frac{7}{2} = 3\frac{1}{2}$

   c. $\frac{1}{4} \times 5 = \frac{5}{4} = 1\frac{1}{4}$

   d. $\frac{1}{5} \times 9 = \frac{9}{5} = 1\frac{4}{5}$

4. The four figures are the same size.
   The set of figures is cut into 5 equal parts.
   a. Shade $(\frac{3}{5} \times 4)$
   b. Show that $\frac{3}{5} \times 4$ is 12 fifths.
      3 rows of fifths, with 4 fifths in each row, are shaded.
      3 × 4 fifths are shaded. 12 fifths are shaded.

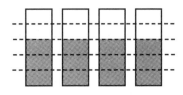

5. Multiply:
   a. $\frac{3}{4} \times 5 = \frac{15}{4} = 3\frac{3}{4}$

   b. $\frac{2}{3} \times 8 = \frac{16}{3} = 5\frac{1}{3}$

   c. $\frac{5}{7} \times 6 = \frac{30}{7} = 4\frac{2}{7}$

   d. $\frac{2}{5} \times 7 = \frac{14}{5} = 2\frac{4}{5}$

6. a. The multiplication to the right
      may be done in three steps.
      Show how.

   b. You also may put the three steps together.
      Show how.

$3\frac{2}{5} \times 4$

a. 1. $\underline{3 \times 4 = 12}$
   2. $\underline{\frac{2}{5} \times 4 = \frac{8}{5} = 1\frac{3}{5}}$
   3. $\underline{12 + 1\frac{3}{5} = 13\frac{3}{5}}$
b. $\underline{3\frac{2}{5} \times 4 = 12\frac{8}{5} = 13\frac{3}{5}}$

Level 15

© Copyright by L. George Saad

7. Multiply:
   a. $2\frac{1}{5} \times 3 = 6\frac{3}{5}$
   b. $6\frac{2}{5} \times 4 = 24\frac{8}{5} = 25\frac{3}{5}$
   c. $9\frac{1}{3} \times 6 = 54\frac{6}{3} = 56$
   d. $5\frac{3}{4} \times 7 = 35\frac{21}{4} = 40\frac{1}{4}$

8. Mark makes \$900 a month.
   He saves $\frac{2}{15}$ of his income.
   How much does he save in one year?

   a. $\frac{2}{15} \times \$900 = \$120$
   b. $12 \times \$120 = \$1,440$

9. $\frac{3}{20}$ of the school is absent.
   There are 800 students in the school.
   How many students are present?

   a. $\frac{3}{20} \times 800 = 120$
   b. $800 - 120 = 680$

10. Sam is $1\frac{1}{3}$ times as tall as Jack.
    Jack is 4 feet tall.
    How tall is Sam in feet and inches?

    a. $1\frac{1}{3} \times 4 = 4\frac{4}{3} = 5\frac{1}{3}$
    b. Sam is 5 feet and 4 inches tall

11. The figure is divided into thirds, and 1 third is cut into 5 equal parts.
    a. Shade $(\frac{1}{5} \times \frac{1}{3})$ of the figure.
    b. Shade $(\frac{4}{5} \times \frac{1}{3})$ of the figure.

    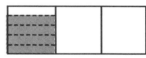

12. The figure is divided into fifths, and 2 fifths are cut into 4 equal parts.
    a. Shade $(\frac{1}{4} \times \frac{2}{5})$ of the figure.
    b. Shade $(\frac{3}{4} \times \frac{2}{5})$ of the figure.

    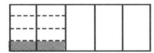
    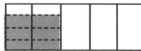

13. The figure is divided into thirds, and
    1 third is cut into 2 equal parts.
    a. Shade $(\frac{1}{2} \times \frac{1}{3})$ of the figure.
    b. Show that $\frac{1}{2} \times \frac{1}{3}$ is the same as $\frac{1}{2 \times 3}$
    We cut each of the other thirds into 2 equal parts.
    The whole is now made of 2 rows, with 3 parts in each row.
    The whole is made of (2 x 3) equal parts.
    One of these parts is shaded $\frac{1}{2 \times 3}$ of the whole is shaded.

14. Multiply:
    a. $\frac{1}{3} \times \frac{1}{2} = \frac{1}{6}$
    b. $\frac{1}{5} \times \frac{1}{4} = \frac{1}{20}$
    c. $\frac{1}{2} \times \frac{1}{5} = \frac{1}{10}$
    d. $\frac{1}{5} \times \frac{1}{3} = \frac{1}{15}$
    e. $\frac{1}{7} \times \frac{1}{5} = \frac{1}{35}$
    f. $\frac{1}{6} \times \frac{1}{8} = \frac{1}{48}$

© Copyright by L. George Saad

Level 15

15. The figure is divided into fourths, and

    3 fourths are cut into 5 equal parts.

    a. Shade $(\frac{1}{5} \times \frac{3}{4})$ of the figure.

    b. Show that $\frac{1}{5} \times \frac{3}{4}$ is the same as $\frac{3}{5 \times 4}$

    We cut the other fourth into 5 equal parts.

    The whole is now made of 5 rows with 4 parts in each row: (5 x 4) equal parts.

    3 of these parts are shaded. $\frac{3}{5 \times 4}$ of the whole is shaded.

16. Multiply:

    a. $\frac{3}{4} \times \frac{1}{2} = \frac{3}{8}$ b. $\frac{2}{5} \times \frac{1}{3} = \frac{2}{15}$ c. $\frac{3}{8} \times \frac{1}{4} = \frac{3}{32}$

    d. $\frac{2}{9} \times \frac{1}{3} = \frac{2}{27}$ e. $\frac{7}{8} \times \frac{1}{5} = \frac{7}{40}$ f. $\frac{3}{10} \times \frac{1}{10} = \frac{3}{100} = 0.03$

17. The figure is divided into thirds, and

    2 thirds are cut into 5 equal parts.

    a. Shade $(\frac{4}{5} \times \frac{2}{3})$ of the figure.

    b. Show that $\frac{4}{5} \times \frac{2}{3}$ is the same as $\frac{4 \times 2}{5 \times 3}$

    We cut the other third into 5 equal parts.

    The whole is now made of 5 rows with 3 parts in each row: (5 x 3) equal parts.

    The shaded area is made of 4 rows, with 2 parts in each row. (4 x 2) equal parts.

    The shaded area is $\frac{4 \times 2}{5 \times 3}$ of the whole.

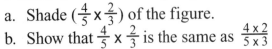

18. Multiply:

    a. $\frac{4}{5} \times \frac{2}{3} = \frac{8}{15}$ b. $\frac{3}{4} \times \frac{3}{5} = \frac{9}{20}$ c. $\frac{3}{10} \times \frac{7}{10} = \frac{21}{100} = 0.21$

    d. $\frac{2}{9} \times \frac{4}{5} = \frac{8}{45}$ e. $\frac{3}{5} \times \frac{2}{5} = \frac{6}{25}$ f. $\frac{9}{10} \times \frac{3}{10} = \frac{27}{100} = 0.27$

19. a. What multiplication does the picture show? $\frac{1}{3} \times 2\frac{1}{2}$

    b. Find the answer: $\frac{1}{3} \times 2\frac{1}{2} = \frac{1}{3} \times \frac{5}{2} = \frac{5}{6}$

20. Multiply:

    a. $\frac{5}{6} \times 1\frac{1}{4} = \frac{5}{6} \times \frac{5}{4} = \frac{25}{24} = 1\frac{1}{24}$

    b. $\frac{4}{5} \times 2\frac{1}{3} = \frac{4}{5} \times \frac{7}{3} = \frac{20}{15} = 1\frac{13}{15}$

21. a. What multiplication does the picture show? $1\frac{1}{2} \times \frac{3}{5}$

    b. Find the answer: $1\frac{1}{2} \times \frac{3}{5} = \frac{3}{2} \times \frac{3}{5} = \frac{9}{10}$

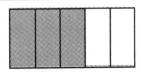

22. Multiply:

    a. $1\frac{1}{2} \times \frac{3}{4} = \frac{3}{2} \times \frac{3}{4} = \frac{9}{8} = 1\frac{1}{8}$

    b. $3\frac{1}{3} \times \frac{2}{3} = \frac{10}{3} \times \frac{2}{3} = \frac{20}{9} = 2\frac{2}{9}$

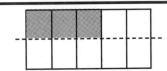

Level 15   © Copyright by L. George Saad

23. a. What multiplication does the picture represent?
    b. Find the answer: $3\frac{1}{2} \times 1\frac{4}{5}$

    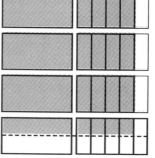

$$3\frac{1}{2} \times 1\frac{4}{5} = \frac{7}{2} \times \frac{9}{5} = \frac{63}{10} = 6\frac{3}{10}$$

24. Multiply:
    a. $3\frac{1}{2} \times 2\frac{1}{3} = \frac{7}{2} \times \frac{7}{3} = \frac{49}{6} = 8\frac{1}{6}$
    b. $2\frac{3}{4} \times 3\frac{1}{2} = \frac{11}{4} \times \frac{7}{2} = \frac{77}{8} = 9\frac{5}{8}$
    c. $6\frac{2}{3} \times 2\frac{1}{3} = \frac{20}{3} \times \frac{7}{3} = \frac{140}{9} = 15\frac{5}{9}$

25. Multiply:

a. 3.5 x 1.7	b. 6.4 x 0.98	c. 0.24 x 1.25
5.95	6.272	0.3000

26. Multiply the simplified way:
    a. $4\frac{4}{5} \times 1\frac{1}{9} = \frac{24}{5} \times \frac{10}{9} = \frac{8}{1} \times \frac{2}{3} = \frac{16}{3} = 5\frac{1}{3}$
    b. $9\frac{1}{6} \times 1\frac{4}{5} = \frac{55}{6} \times \frac{9}{5} = \frac{11}{2} \times \frac{3}{1} = \frac{33}{2} = 16\frac{1}{2}$
    c. $2\frac{7}{10} \times 4\frac{1}{6} = \frac{27}{10} \times \frac{25}{6} = \frac{9}{2} \times \frac{5}{2} = \frac{45}{4} = 11\frac{1}{4}$
    d. $3\frac{1}{9} \times 2\frac{5}{8} = \frac{28}{9} \times \frac{21}{8} = \frac{7}{3} \times \frac{7}{2} = \frac{49}{6} = 8\frac{1}{6}$

27. Mom bought $2\frac{1}{4}$ lb. of meat.
    She cooked $\frac{2}{3}$ the meat she bought.
    How much meat did she cook?

    $\frac{2}{3} \times 2\frac{1}{4} = \frac{2}{3} \times \frac{9}{4} = \frac{3}{2} = 1\frac{1}{2}$ lb.

28. A man is $5\frac{1}{3}$ times as old as his son.
    The son is $7\frac{1}{2}$ years old.
    How old is the father?

    $5\frac{1}{3} \times 7\frac{1}{2} = \frac{16}{3} \times \frac{15}{2} = 40$ years

29. One sheet of paper weighs 6.25 grams.
    a. Find the weight of a package
       of 500 sheets in kilograms.
    b. Find the weight of $1\frac{2}{5}$ packages.

    $500 \times 6.25 = 3125$ gm $= 3.125$ kg.
    $1\frac{2}{5} \times 3.125 = 1.4 \times 3.125 = 4.375$ kg.

30. a. What is the reciprocal of $\frac{8}{9}$?

    $\frac{9}{8}$

    b. A is the reciprocal of B.
       How are A and B related?

    $A \times B = 1$

© Copyright by L. George Saad

Level 15

31. A, B, and C are three numbers.

    If A is $2\frac{2}{3}$, B is 3, and A + B + C is 10,

    What number is C?

$C = 10 - (2\frac{2}{3} + 3)$
$= 10 - (2\frac{8}{12} + 3\frac{9}{4})$
$= 10 - (5\,1\frac{7}{12})$
$= 10 - 6\frac{6}{12}$
$= 3\frac{7}{12}$

32. If N + 2 = $6\frac{1}{3}$, then what number is N?

$N = 6\frac{1}{3} - (2)$
$= 6\frac{4}{12} - (2\frac{9}{12})$
$= 3\frac{7}{12}$

33. You multiplied a number by 8, and then divided by 6. The answer was $2\frac{1}{3}$.

    What was the number?

$(2\frac{1}{3} \times 6) \div 8$
$= (12\frac{6}{3}) \div 8$
$= 14 \div 8$
$= 1\frac{6}{8}$
$= 1$

34. The sum of two numbers is $6\frac{1}{3}$. One number is 3.

    What is the other number?

$6\frac{1}{3} - 3$
$= 6\frac{2}{6} - 3\frac{3}{6}$
$= 2\frac{5}{6}$

35. Find the answer:

$(\frac{1}{2} \times \frac{1}{3}) + (\frac{2}{3} \times \frac{3}{4})$

$(\frac{1}{6}) + (\frac{6}{12})$
$= \frac{2}{12} + \frac{6}{12}$
$= \frac{8}{12}$
$= \frac{2}{3}$

36. What number do you multiply by $\frac{2}{3}$ for the answer to be $8\frac{1}{3}$?

$\frac{3}{2} \times (8\frac{1}{3})$
$= \frac{3}{2} \times 2\frac{5}{3}$
$= 7\frac{5}{6}$
$= 12$

© Copyright by L. George Saad